# EARTHQUAKES and
# FAULTS in
# SAN DIEGO COUNTY

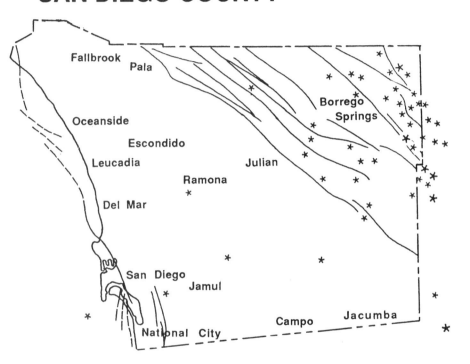

## PHILIP KERN

Professor of Geology
San Diego State University

The Pickle Press
San Diego

## ON THE COVER

The cover is adapted from one of Tom Rockwell's illustrations of a trench exposure of the Rose Canyon fault. In such disemboweled views the fault is shown to consist near the surface of an upward-spreading network of intersecting fractures — a flower structure.

The title page map shows major earthquake epicenters and the active faults of San Diego County.

Designed and produced by the author.

A Pickle Press book

ISBN    0-9622845-1-3

This book is for Colin — for seeing the beauty, for hearing the music, for reading the words, for playing the games, for laughing and whistling, and for walking with me in wild places.

## PREFACE TO THE 1993 EDITION

The proliferation of interest in, and knowledge of, San Diego County's faults and earthquake history has accelerated into the 1990's, and I have attempted to incorporate all available information into this revised and expanded edition. Tom Rockwell and his co-workers have finally shown conclusively that the Rose Canyon fault is active, and they have provided definitive information on its rate of movement and expected earthquake magnitudes. This information has been included along with new detailed maps of parts of the Rose Canyon, Elsinore, and San Jacinto fault zones, and the County's earthquake history is brought up to date through early 1993. New chapters have been added on the dramatic increase in southern California's earthquake activity during the past decade, including the Landers earthquake sequence, and on the Special Studies Zones that have been designated on the Rose Canyon fault. The burgeoning literature on San Diego County earthquakes has doubled the list of entries in the Bibliography.

This book still serves largely as a non-technical guide to earthquakes and faults throughout San Diego County. I have attempted to present geologic concepts in such a way that they can be understood by someone with little or no prior knowledge in the science. Included are a review of the major quakes that have shaken the County since 1800, maps of principal earthquake epicenters and of all major active faults, and summaries of probable future earthquake activity on these faults as it has been estimated by geologists and seismologists. The book also is intended to serve as a field guide to these faults, and there are descriptions and illustrations of easily accessible places where you can go to see them. I hope that you will gain from such excursions a greater knowledge and understanding of earthquakes and faults in San Diego County and a better appreciation of our likely earthquake future and the measures one can take in preparation for those quakes to come.

Please be careful. Among the various hazards posed by the faults are the perils encountered in looking at them, and the author cannot be held responsible for accidents that may result from visits to the locations described here. Some of the exposures are in high, treacherous cliffs that readily shed boulders, people, and other objects. Some are adjacent to roads and streets that carry fast, heavy traffic; this is especially true at road cuts on mountain and desert highways. When you go looking for faults, watch your step and keep an eye on vehicles, falling rocks, and other projectiles. Be especially careful at highway road cuts to stay out of traffic lanes and not to obstruct or distract drivers.

San Diego<br>
May 1, 1993

## SOURCES

The information in this book has been compiled from papers published in geological and seismological journals and from reports prepared for various government agencies. The principal sources for assessment of fault activity and estimates of future earthquakes include reports by Leighton and Associates (1983) and Woodward-Clyde Consultants (l986) and articles by Bob McEuen and Jerry Pinckney (1972), by Cal Tech geologist Steven Wesnousky (1986), and by SIO and SDSU geoscientists John Anderson, Duncan Agnew, and Tom Rockwell (1989). Parts of the text were excerpted from a report (Kern, 1987) that I compiled for the San Diego County Office of Disaster Preparedness.

What you read here, then, is not based on my interpretations and I do not claim authority or responsibility for it; rather it is a compilation and synthesis of the views of those professional·geologists and seismologists who are authorities on earthquake hazard in San Diego County, and it is based entirely on information that is available to the public from a variety of sources.

## ACKNOWLEDGEMENTS

Many people have contributed in a variety of ways to the completion of this book. Much of what is known about earthquake hazard in San Diego County has come from the research of my colleague, Tom Rockwell, and his many collaborators on investigations of the San Jacinto, Elsinore, Rose Canyon, and Agua Blanca and offshore fault systems. Tom has given many hours of his time in discussion of the geologic and seismologic character of these fault zones and has also provided several of the illustrations used here.

Others who have made substantial contributions include Duncan Agnew, Research Seismologist at Scripps Institution of Oceanography; Steve Day, Eckis Professor of Seismology at San Diego State University; Monte Marshall, Professor of Geology at SDSU; and Mike Reichle, Seismologist with the California Division of Mines and Geology. Several illustrations were made available by Professor Marshall and by another colleague, Rick Miller.

Lowell Lindsay of Sunbelt Publications has been especially helpful in facilitating the preparation of this new edition. Both Ed Zimmerly and Rene Wagemakers helped with technical and design questions. Among the many community leaders whose efforts on behalf of earthquake preparedness have helped to inspire this  work, the principal individuals are Dan Eberle, Director of the County Office of Disaster Preparedness; Jan Decker, now with the County Water Authority; and Mayor Susan Golding, who as County Supervisor created the Committee on Earthquake Preparedness. Others who have provided encouragement include Karl Anderson and David Dunn, energetic members of the Tecolote Canyon Citizens Advisory Committee; members of the Mission Valley and San Diego Exchange Clubs; Don Prisby, Pete Jungers, and Nancy Acevedo of the Parks and Recreation Department; sixth district City Councilwoman Valerie Stallings and her aide Kathleen Higgins; and Bruce Bailey and other students of geological sciences at SDSU. I thank you and all the others who have been involved in the ongoing efforts to understand better the earthquakes and faults of San Diego County.

## THE AUTHOR

This book and its predecessors were written as a result of the author's interest in the teaching of geology to general audiences. The book is intended, therefore, to serve as a comprehensible field guide to faults and as a home or schoolroom guide to earthquake causes, characteristics, and history. For a decade it has served these purposes for individuals as well as for classes offered to public and private organizations, museums, university extension programs, and in the schools. Schools also are the target audience for field trips and hands-on programs on earthquakes and other aspects of geology and natural history that are now in the planning stages.

The author received the doctorate in geology from the University of California at Los Angeles and has been Professor of Geological Sciences at San Diego State University for a quarter century. He has spent more than a decade mapping faults as part of a more inclusive study of the Pleistocene geologic history of coastal San Diego County. Technical publications include articles on San Diego fossils, marine terraces, and Pleistocene deformation, while non-technical writings have appeared in Sierra, San Diego Home and Garden, Environment Southwest, and the San Diego Tribune. Since the mid 1980's Professor Kern has been extensively involved in San Diego City and County programs for earthquake preparedness.

# CONTENTS

# FAULT MAPS

# EARTHQUAKES AND FAULTS IN SAN DIEGO COUNTY

## I. EARTHQUAKE ACTIVITY HAS INCREASED RECENTLY IN SOUTHERN CALIFORNIA

Earthquake activity increased dramatically in coastal San Diego County beginning in 1984, and that increased activity has continued through the time of this writing early in 1993. During this time the rate of earthquake occurrence has doubled over that during the preceding 50 years (Heaton and Jones, 1989). The quakes have been small ones, except for the 1986 magnitude-5.3 Oceanside temblor, which triggered aftershocks for more than three years. Also during this time three different clusters of small earthquakes have erupted along the Rose Canyon fault zone under San Diego Bay — first in June, 1985; then from August through September, 1986 (beginning three weeks after the July Oceanside quake); and finally in September, 1987 (Magistrale, in press). A similar increase in earthquake frequency began in the Los Angeles and Santa Monica basins in 1986. As yet there is no explanation for this sudden increase in seismic activity throughout coastal southen California, but similar episodes appear to have preceded the 1906 and 1989 San Francisco earthquakes and the 1948 quake near Desért Hot Springs.

During the same time a marked increase in the number of moderate to large earthquakes (magnitudes greater than 5 and 6) has occurred throughout the broader southern California region. This trend began with the north Palm Springs temblor of magnitude 5.6 on July 8, 1986. It continued in 1987 with the magnitude-5.9 Whittier Earthquake in October, and on November 23 and 24 with quakes of magnitude 6.2 and 6.6 in Imperial County's Superstition Hills. Now this series has been extended into 1992 by California's most impressive earthquake sequence in 40 years. The sequence began on April 22 with the magnitude-6.2 Joshua Tree quake, centered only 12 miles southeast of Landers. On June 28 the Landers 7.4 quake itself was followed three hours later and 20 miles to the west by the Big Bear quake of magnitude 6.3.

Felt as far away as Denver and Boise, the Landers Earthquake was the strongest in California since the 1952 magnitude-7.7 Tehachapi quake, and except for that one and San Francisco's 1906 quake it was the third most powerful shock here since 1872. The Landers and Joshua Tree quakes together ruptured the ground for a total of nearly 60 miles; rupture in the Landers quake alone was 40 miles, and the maximum observed fault movement was 20 feet. The illustration shows a line of ruptured ground along the trace of the Emerson fault where it crosses Galway Lake Road, 20 miles north-northwest of Landers. Rupture occurred on five different faults in this earthquake; that was quite a surprise, for it had been thought from past experience that fault rupture was confined to single faults or even to individual segments of faults.

Even more remarkable was the widespread triggering of activity on other faults both near and far. The Landers quake produced three-quarters of an inch of fault creep on the San Andreas fault in the Mecca Hills area, some 40 miles to the southeast. Then within minutes after Landers, hundreds of small quakes erupted in volcanic areas near Mammoth Lakes and Mount Shasta (Toppozada, 1993). Seismic activity also increased in the western Mojave

2

Desert and at several other sites, including Yellowstone National Park, 700 miles away.

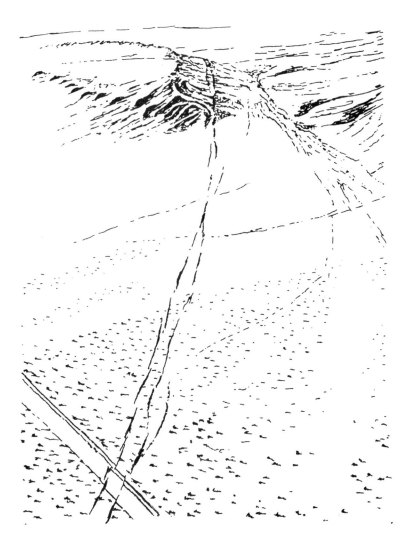

Ground ruptured by the Landers earthquake. EMERSON FAULT at Galway Lake Road, 20 miles from Landers

For such a powerful shock there was relatively little damage. Though there were several hundred injuries, a few of them serious, only one death was attributed to the earthquake. More than a hundred homes and thirty businesses were destroyed in Los Angeles and Riverside counties, and initial figures suggest approximately 100 million dollars in damage. Near the epicentral region chimneys toppled, windows were broken, counter-top appliances and other objects were thrown to the floor, pictures fell, and power lines came down.

The northeastern corner of San Diego County is 45 miles south of the Landers epicenter, and downtown San Diego is 70 miles away. Though the quake was felt strongly throughout the County, there was little serious damage here. The Borrego Springs Airport lost power briefly, as did 25,000 homes and businesses across the region, 6000 of them in San Diego. Rides were closed at Sea World and the Zoo, and KFSD radio was off the air for an hour. Cracks in the roadbed of I-5 in National City resulted in a brief closure to traffic. The Hyatt Islandia Hotel at Mission Bay was evacuated because of cracked concrete walls and broken water pipes. Plaster walls were cracked in the U. S. Grant Hotel, but there were no serious injuries or damage.

# II. THE BIG ONES STRIKE SAN DIEGO COUNTY

## NOVEMBER 23, 1800

The first of three powerful nineteenth-century and earlier earthquakes struck what was then a sparsely populated coastal region. The few written accounts tell of cracking of adobe walls in the mission buildings both at San Diego and at San Juan Capistrano. Such extensive damage at widely separated locations suggests that the quake must have been at least magnitude 6.5; it was even higher if the epicenter was away from the coastal zone, either offshore or to the east.

## MAY 27, 1862

The most destructive of San Diego's nineteenth-century quakes cracked the walls of Old Town's Pico and Bandini Adobes and the Whaley House, as well as the stone lighthouse on Point Loma. Wooden buildings sagged throughout the town, while door hinges and windows were shattered. Pendulum clocks stopped, the Army Depot bell was set ringing, and crockery smashed to the floors. Near the river and on the beach cracks gaped in the earth, while water surged up on the shore in both places.

The initial shaking lasted for several seconds. Then, after a few moments of quiet, there was a second shock. From newspaper accounts, letters, and other written records the shaking and destruction in San Diego have been measured at VI to VII on the Modified Mercalli scale of earthquake intensity (described in chapter VIII). The epicenter may have been in the Rose Canyon fault zone directly under San Diego, in which case the damage it caused suggests a magnitude of about 6.0. Or it may have been further away — offshore to the west or southwest of the city, perhaps in the Coronado Bank or San Diego Trough fault zones — indicating an even greater magnitude. Aftershocks continued into the following year.

## FEBRUARY 23, 1892

The strongest earthquake recorded during historic times in the San Diego region struck in northern Mexico just beyond the southeastern corner of the County. The ground was cracked for a distance of more than 12 miles along the Laguna Salada fault, and at one place a wall of rock rose twelve feet out of the desert floor. The illustration, which was provided by Tom Rockwell and will appear in the article by Mueller and Rockwell, shows several geologists surveying this dramatic scarp. At Carrizo Stage Station several adobe buildings were destroyed. A wall was shaken down at Campo, and others were cracked. Small objects were overturned at Julian and at Escondido, where goods also were shaken off storeroom shelves. A stone kiln was cracked at Jamul, and in San Diego many buildings were cracked and ceilings unplastered, as frantic citizens scattered into the streets.

LAGUNA SALADA FAULT

This earthquake, which was felt in Needles, Visalia, and Santa Barbara, is estimated to have had a magnitude close to 7. It produced stronger shaking throughout San Diego County than has any other quake, with Mercalli intensities of VIII and IX (see chapter VIII) in the southeastern corner of the County. The city itself, 70 miles away, was shaken nearly as strongly as it had been in 1862.

All three of these quakes — 1800, 1862, and 1892 — produced shaking intensities as high as VII in the coastal area. A comparable earthquake today would cause extensive damage to most poorly built structures. Unreinforced masonry walls, chimneys, and building fronts are likely to be cracked or to collapse completely. Plaster and stucco would fall and windows and furniture be broken. We could expect prodigious breaking of dishes, glassware, knick-knacks, pictures, and other unattached objects. Nearly everyone would be frightened, and some might be knocked off their feet. These three were major destructive earthquakes, but in fact San Diego is likely to suffer even more powerful quakes in the future.

## 199?

(The following account is adapted from Reichle, 1990 and 1991, and from Michael Grant's March 27, 1989, column in the San Diego Union.)

The most powerful earthquake within San Diego County struck on the Silver Strand fault, a part of the Rose Canyon zone, just offshore from Coronado. The quake registered 6.8 on the Richter scale, and strong shaking continued for 15 seconds in the coastal areas.

The initial shock struck with terrifying effect. Throughout the coastal zone people were flung to the ground, and cars bounced into the air and careened out of control. Several vehicles plunged off the Coronado Bridge when the approaches broke away in liquefied bayshore sands and muds, and hundreds of others crashed off collapsing interchanges and bridges. An Amtrak train was derailed when the roadbed disintegrated on liquefying river-bottom sediments near Old Town. Approaching aircraft were immediately diverted from Lindbergh Field's shattered runways.

The ground was ruptured where the fault crosses Silver Strand on the southeast edge of Coronado, but no buildings were directly affected. The strong and prolonged shaking, however, caused massive damage, especially in the low areas of unconsolidated ground along the coast, which was subjected throughout to shaking intensity of IX (chapter VIII). Intensity VIII shaking, weaker but still stronger than that in any previous quake here, extended through Chula Vista, National City, western La Mesa, Tierra Santa, Kearny Mesa, La Jolla, and Del Mar. Many houses and other buildings were destroyed or severely damaged in Coronado, Imperial Beach, National City, Chula Vista, and Loma Portal. Chimneys fell throughout that area, walls cracked, and buildings were thrown from their foundations. Facades, cornices, and parapets fell from many of the old buildings in the downtown area, strewing tons of bricks and glass into the streets. Windows were smashed everywhere, heavy furniture was overturned, and nothing remained on shelves.

Liquefaction of unconsolidated, water-saturated sands and muds along the waterfront and in the lower reaches of river valleys contributed to the destruction. Beyond the epicentral area further damage was caused by a number of large landslides, especially along the north side of Mission Valley and above Rose Canyon on the steep east slope of Mount Soledad, but in many other places as well.

In addition to the immediate widespread destruction of property, there was also severe and prolonged disruption of communication and transportation facilities, of utility lines into the city, and of the operations of most emergency response agencies. Mains were shaken apart throughout the city, leaving some areas without water for as long as four weeks. One of the city's five aqueducts also was broken and was not repaired for several months, reducing the overall city water supply by 20 per cent. The water shortages reduced electrical output of the South Bay Power Plant. Electrical transmission lines and substations went down in hundreds of places, and power was not widely available until three weeks later. In addition, the lack of water severely impaired the operation of the Point Loma Sewage Facility, and rupture of sewage lines throughout the city left raw sewage to pour into San Diego Bay for four months. Natural gas lines were broken in many places along the coast, and some areas were without gas for more than two weeks. The gas pipeline to Coronado was broken under the Bay, and four months passed before it's replacement was complete.

Telephone lines were unavailable for several days because of shaking down of lines and switching equipment as well as overloading by emergency calls. Medical, fire, police, and other response agencies were severely restricted by disruption of communications systems and impassable roads.

The Coronado Bridge was closed for half a year because of destruction of both its approaches, and route 75 on Silver Strand was restricted to emergency traffic only for the first few days. Interchanges were destroyed or badly damaged at the intersections of I-8 and 163, I-5 and 163, I-5 and 805, and 163 and 94  Interstate 5 was closed from Balboa Avenue to Palm Avenue because of numerous failures of the roadway and bridges. Many bridges also came down on both I-5 and old route 101 across coastal valleys north of the City. As a result of these and countless other disruptions, traffic was at a standstill for a week and did not return to something like normal conditions for several months.  The Santa Fe rail line northward out of the city was blocked by many landslides and by collapse or weakening of bridges across coastal valleys, and that service was not restored for a month. Extensive subsidence and cracking of the runways and loss of electrical power closed Lindbergh Field. It was available for emergency flights within a few days but was closed to regular commercial traffic for two weeks.

Even beyond the destruction caused by the earthquake directly, considerable hardship was experienced because most people were unprepared for this earthquake. This was in spite of the fact that the nature and extent of the damage were very much as had been predicted in earthquake planning studies carried out years ago (for example, see Reichle, 1990 and 1991, and Grant, 1989). Many San Diegans seem to have been taken by surprise, believing that the preceding century of relative quiescence in San Diego County assured that there is no serious earthquake hazard here.

Now that the historical earthquake record has been well documented, however, it is clearly important that this misconception be corrected and that individuals, businesses, and governments alike prepare for the inevitable earthquakes to come.

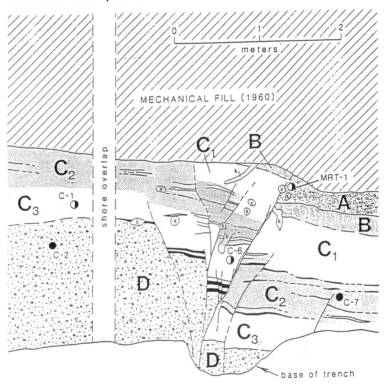

ROSE CANYON FAULT, trench exposure

# III. TWO SPECIAL STUDIES ZONES HAVE BEEN DESIGNATED ON THE ROSE CANYON FAULT

In recent years it has been shown conclusively in two different places that the Rose Canyon fault zone is active. One result of these discoveries has been the designation of two Special Studies Zones, a measure that imposes a number of specific requirements on new developments along these faults.

During the 1984 excavation for the foundation of the San Diego Police Administration and Technical Center on Broadway and E Street between 14th and 15th Avenues, several active strands of the Rose Canyon fault were uncovered. The original plan for the building layout was modified in order to avoid these faults.

Then in 1990 and 1991 trenches that were cut across the fault near the mouth of Rose Canyon showed that it also is active in that area. The accompanying illustration, which was provided by Tom Rockwell, shows the many intersecting fractures of the fault in this trench and the displacement of sand and mud layers across these fractures. As a result of these studies, two segments of the Rose Canyon fault — one a quarter mile long through downtown San Diego and a longer one from La Jolla Shores through Clairemont — were designated Special Studies Zones on November 1, 1991.

The Alquist-Priolo Special Studies Zones Act was passed by the California Legislature in 1972 as a result of the devastation caused by the 1971 Sylmar earthquake. Designation of such Special Studies Zones serves as an official notification of the probability of ground rupture during future earthquakes. Where such zones are designated, no building may be constructed on the line of the fault, and before any construction is allowed a geologic study must be conducted to determine the locations of all active fault lines in the zone. The Rose Canyon fault is the third so designated in San Diego County, after the Elsinore and San Jacinto faults.

In 1988 the City of San Diego Building Code already had been amended to require a geologic report before construction of certain types of buildings in city-designated geologic hazard zones. By the mid 1980's the San Diego Municipal Code also contained an ordinance requiring geologic study of sites that may be susceptible to earthquake-induced liquefaction. This was the first such law in any California city, but legislation was enacted in 1990 requiring State designation of Special Studies Zones in areas of potential liquefaction. This State legislation has not yet been fully implemented.

It has further been recommended by the Structural Engineers Association of California that the city of San Diego change its minimum building construction standards from those required for the Uniform- Building Code's earthquake hazard zone 3 to those of zone 4 — the highest fault hazard designation. Because of the exceedingly high costs that would be incurred as a result of such a measure, which would require strengthening of more than 700 large masonry buildings in San Diego, this change has not been adopted as of early 1993. It is likely, however, that the State will mandate this change with the 1994 edition of the Uniform Building Code by including all of San Diego County in zone 4.

# IV. FAULTS AND EARTHQUAKES ARE CAUSED BY MOVEMENTS OF EARTH'S LITHOSPHERE PLATES PAST ONE ANOTHER

Earthquakes occur here because San Diego County occupies a broad belt of great instability in Earth's crusty skin. Deeper layers of the planet (in the mantle), because of extreme heat and pressure, are not solid but behave as a thick fluid, like cold honey, that flows about under the brittle crust. The crust is broken thereby into great plates, 40 to 50 miles thick, that float ponderously about on the slowly swirling currents beneath.

The boundaries between adjacent moving plates are fault zones, in which the faults that we see at the surface extend down through the crust. Friction prevents adjoining plates from moving past one another most of the time, but continual motion of their fluid underpinnings constantly increases the pressure that is exerted along the faults. When the resising force eventually is overcome, the two plates lurch abruptly past one another, sending waves of motion — an earthquake — out across the planet.

Earth's crust under the Pacific Ocean is on one such plate, the crust of North America on another. The Pacific plate is gliding northward, at several inches each year, past North America. The boundary between these plates, however, is not a simple one. It consists rather of a broad belt that is broken into long, irregular slices by a series of more-or-less parallel faults. The accompanying map shows the chief fractures of this series, from the San Andreas fault on the east to the San Clemente fault on the west.

While many of the most devastating earthquakes in California have resulted from movements on the San Andreas fault, as in San Francisco in 1906 and at Fort Tejon in 1857 (both magnitude 7.9), the entire zone is prone to convulsion. The San Jacinto fault, which is an Imperial Valley branch of the San Andreas, has spawned 13

13

quakes of magnitude 6 or higher in the past century. The Elsinore fault has had a somewhat less tumultuous recent history, with only one quake greater than magnitude 5 during the past 50 years. Similarly the Rose Canyon fault and those offshore as far as San Clemente Island also remain active. San Clemente Island had a quake of magnitude 5.9 in 1951, and in 1986 there was another of magnitude 5.3 on the Coronado Bank fault off Solana Beach. San Diego County thus lies within a broad belt of shattered crust that is subject throughout to violent quaking as its western margin jerks northward past the eastern one.

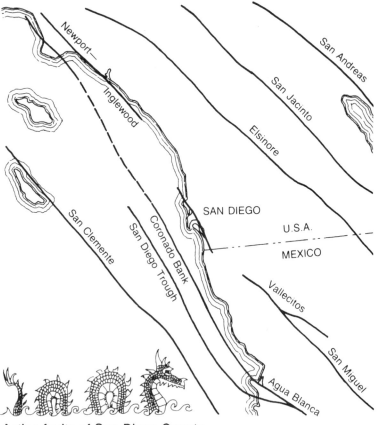

Active faults of San Diego County

# V. EARTHQUAKE MAGNITUDE IS RELATED TO FAULT LENGTH, LENGTH OF FAULT RUPTURE, MAXIMUM AMOUNT OF FAULT MOVEMENT, RATE OF MOVEMENT, AND TIME INTERVAL BETWEEN QUAKES

The point at which the initial rupture occurs on a fault, and from which the earthquake waves radiate outward, is called the focus, or hypocenter.  The epicenter is the point on the earth's surface directly above the focus.  If the distance the rocks move past one another (the amount of slip) is large at the focus, say several to many feet, then much energy is released and the earthquake is of large magnitude.  The fault plane also will  be ruptured (will slip) over a large part of its length and depth.  It may rupture at the ground surface for distances up to hundreds of miles.  If on the other hand the earthquake is of small magnitude or its focus is deep, the rupture may not reach the surface at all.

The amount of slip varies along the fault plane, with a maximum amount at the focus decreasing in all directions to zero at the edges of the zone of rupture.  In the 1906 San Francisco earthquake (magnitude 7.9), for example, the San Andreas fault ruptured at the surface for 270 miles, from near Cape Mendocino to San Juan Bautista. The largest amount of horizontal slip at the surface was measured in Marin County, where a road and a fence were offset by 20 feet, while at San Juan Bautista slip ranged from a few inches to zero.  In the more powerful 1964 Alaska earthquake (magnitude 9.2) the fault ruptured at the surface for 500 miles.

Generally speaking, then, higher magnitude results from longer surface rupture and greater maximum amount of slip.  Though it varies considerably with the kinds of rocks, with depth of earthquake focus, and with other factors, the relationship between earthquake magnitude, length of surface rupture, and maximum amount of slip is

15

approximately as follows:

| MAGNITUDE | RUPTURE LENGTH | MAXIMUM SLIP |
|-----------|----------------|--------------|
| 5.5 | 2 miles | 1 inch |
| 6.0 | 6 | 3 |
| 6.5 | 1 2 | 1 foot |
| 7.0 | 3 0 | 3 |
| 7.5 | 7 5 | 6 |
| 8.0 | 2 1 0 | 3 3 |
| 8.5 | 6 0 0 | 1 0 0 |

Thus longer faults are capable of producing more powerful earthquakes, and one way of estimating the earthquake hazard of a fault is to determine the maximum magnitude that is likely if it ruptures along its entire length.

The amount of slip that occurs, and resulting earthquake magnitude, also are controlled by a fault's average long-term rate of slip, generally measured by geologists in millimeters per year, and its average earthquake recurrence interval — the time interval between earthquakes. The long-term average slip rate is controlled by the velocity at which the plates are being pulled along by underlying currents, while recurrence interval is influenced by the kinds of rocks, the direction of fault motions, the geometry of the fault plane, and other factors that determine how much stress can build up before rupture occurs. If slip rate is high (more than a few millimeters per year) and recurrence interval is long (hundreds of years or more), a fault will be characterized by infrequent but strong earthquakes. If slip rate is low (less than a few millimeters a year) and recurrence interval is short (tens of years), the fault will be characterized by frequent smaller quakes.

Faults tend to have a characteristic behavior in these regards, and, if their earthquake history is known, then the long-term average earthquake pattern is more-or-less predictable. Many faults seem to have "characteristic" earthquakes all of about the same magnitude, and with a fairly consistent average recurrence interval.

Long faults, though, are unlikely to rupture for their entire lengths in a single earthquake. Rather, they tend to be segmented, with the segments separated from one another by bends, branches, or discontinuous steps to the left or right. It is thought that these discontinuities are surface expressions of deep-seated obstacles to rupture. Earthquakes typically result from rupture of just one or, in some instances, a few segments; thus it is often fault segments whose characteristic earthquake magnitude and recurrence interval are estimated.

Some faults or fault segments may produce earthquakes of magnitude greater than their length would suggest because they become "locked". If a fault bends or steps in such a way that movement is impeded, stress may accumulate for a much longer time than it would on a straight fault. Unusually long recurrence intervals then would be punctuated by unexpectedly powerful earthquakes.

Some faults also appear to have extraordinarily long recurrence intervals — as high as thousands of years and perhaps even tens of thousands of years. It is thought that rocks on opposite sides of faults with exceptionally low slip rates may become annealed, or fused together, with the result that stress builds up to a much higher degree than it normally would. Earthquake magnitudes far out of proportion to fault length can result at just as unexpectedly long intervals. Where such conditions exist, it may be extremely difficult to know when faults have truly become inactive.

Some faults or fault segments "creep", or move more or less continuously; some of these creeping faults also have earthquakes, while others have no quakes at all. A 60-mile-long segment of the San Andreas fault from Hollister to west of Coalinga has been creeping at about one inch a year during historic time.

# VI. MAGNITUDES OF FUTURE EARTHQUAKES ARE ESTIMATED FROM THE HISTORIC RECORD AND FROM GEOLOGIC EVIDENCE FOR THE PREHISTORIC RECORD

Earthquake hazard evaluation requires estimates both of probable magnitude of future earthquakes and of average frequency, or recurrence interval, at which they are likely to occur. This information can be obtained from the historic record, if that record is long enough, or it can be determined from geologic evidence of the prehistoric record. Estimation of locations, magnitudes, and times of occurrence of future earthquakes allows for anticipation of shaking and other damage in a particular place, depending on its distance from the earthquake epicenter and the local geologic conditions.

The most direct evidence for future earthquake hazard is that of the historic record — from experience and from written accounts in newspapers, letters, diaries, journals, mission records, and so on. Residents of San Francisco can expect eventually to experience a repetition of the 1906 earthquake, as those of Anchorage can anticipate another like that of 1964. The sparse accounts we have of the San Diego County earthquakes of 1800, 1862, and 1892 warn us to be prepared for comparable quakes in the future.

If the historic record is long enough to reveal the long-term earthquake behavior of a fault, one can estimate probable magnitude and approximate recurrence interval of future quakes, as faults seem to have "characteristic" earthquakes of about the same maximum magnitude and at more-or-less regular intervals. The principal uncertainty would be in the timing. Some faults have short average recurrence intervals of a few tens of years, while others have quite long intervals, up to at least several hundred years and perhaps in some cases even thousands or tens of thousands of years. There is no way of determining such long intervals from the historic record, as that record is too short. Faults with such long recurrence intervals would be unlikely to have had an earthquake in historic time, so even their characteristic magnitude would not be known directly.

Recurrence intervals are rather uniform on some faults, while on others they may vary widely about the average. One of the more regular southern California faults, for example, is the San Jacinto, which passes through the northeastern corner of San Diego County. It has had 13 earthquakes of magnitude 5.8 to 6.8 since 1899, an average of one every 8 years and with no interval greater than 16 years. Because most faults have much longer recurrence intervals and the historic record in southern California goes back only to around 1800, that record provides little or no information on earthquake recurrence intervals on some of our major faults.

Thus there are limitations to the historic record, but it does provide some information on earthquake recurrence interval, approximate magnitude, fault rupture length, and long-term rates of slip. Where data are well documented, these facts serve as a basis for estimation of a fault's probable future earthquake hazard.

Geologic evidence for the prehistoric earthquake record comes from features such as fault scarps (cliffs formed by movement of one side of the fault above the other side), as in the illustration of the Laguna Salada fault in chapter II; offset streams or rock formations, and displaced beds seen either in natural outcrops or in trenches dug specifically for the purpose of studying faults. Stream channels, for example, are offset in crossing many of southern California's active faults, as in the illustration. In some cases one channel approaches a fault and several leave it on the other side, the separate offsets recording movements in successive earthquakes. Amounts of slip indicated by such offsets can be used to estimate approximate magnitudes of future quakes. If the dates of the past earthquakes can be determined, say by carbon-dating of deposits into which the stream channels are cut, then one can determine earthquake recurrence interval and long-term rate of slip on the fault. Such slip rates also can be calculated if one knows the age of a rock formation that has been displaced a known distance along a fault.

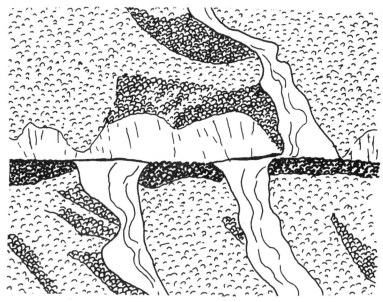

Oblique air view of stream valley offset twice by earthquakes on SAN JACINTO FAULT just east of San Diego County (from photo provided by Tom Rockwell; width of view one-quarter mile)

Another method of obtaining information on prehistoric earthquakes is by digging trenches across faults that cut through deposits of sediments that have been accumulating during recent times, as in ponds and swamps. In such trenches one commonly finds that successively lower, thus older, layers of sand and mud have increasingly greater offsets because they have been displaced by more earthquakes. Here it can be even simpler to determine the dates of those earthquakes by carbon-dating of wood, shell, or other organic materials that were buried in the displaced sediments. Magnitudes of the earthquakes are suggested by the amount of slip, and here too it may be

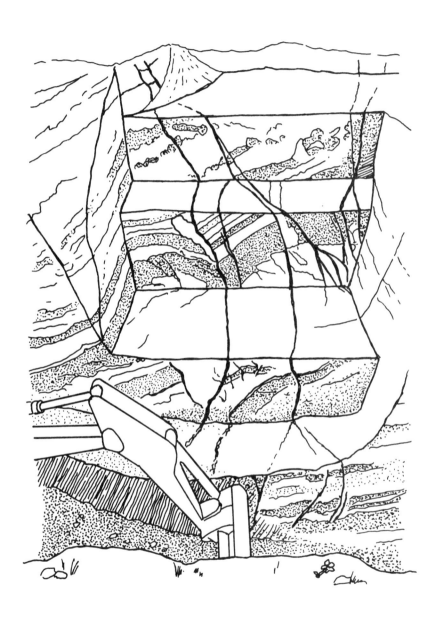

ELSINORE FAULT in trench at Glen Ivy Marsh north of Lake
Elsinore (from photo provided by Tom Rockwell)

21

possible to reconstruct earthquake history — dates, amounts of slip, magnitudes, long-term average slip rates, and average recurrence intervals.

Among a variety of odd sources of information that geologists have found are old trees that are growing on a fault and that were injured or killed by earthquake movements. The date of the disturbance can be obtained from the tree-ring record by comparing it with rings in nearby trees not on the fault. By using these and other kinds of evidence for the longer prehistoric record, it is possible to increase the base of information from which future earthquake risk can be estimated.

Where there is no information on age or magnitude of historic or prehistoric earthquakes, it is more difficult to evaluate earthquake hazard. If there is topographic evidence of recent activity, say in fresh fault scarps, offset streams, or other fault features, one can infer that there is some future earthquake hazard. The relationship between earthquake magnitude and fault length or fault segment length then allows one to make at least a general estimate of likely magnitude.

In any case there is always some uncertainty in estimation of earthquake hazard. Recurrence intervals can vary widely, and faults can alter their behavior. Active faults can become inactive, their previous movements taken up later on other fault zones, and new faults can appear. Important fault features, or entire faults themselves, may not be clearly exposed and thus may remain completely unknown until an earthquake occurs. All the estimates in the following chapters must be regarded as exactly that — estimates of what appear to geologists and seismologists, from existing knowledge, to be the most likely future behavior of the fault in question.

# VII. EARTHQUAKE DAMAGE VARIES WITH MAGNITUDE, DISTANCE FROM EPICENTER, GEOLOGIC CONDITIONS, AND BUILDING CONSTRUCTION; AND IT INCLUDES THE EFFECTS OF GROUND SHAKING AND RUPTURE, LANDSLIDES, TSUNAMIS, AND FIRES

The principal factors that determine the shaking damage caused in a particular place by an earthquake, in addition to magnitude, include the distance from the epicenter, the duration of shaking, the local geologic conditions, and the type and quality of building construction.

Just as the ripples spreading from a stone thrown in a pond grow smaller as they travel farther away, earthquake waves also decrease in size and energy as they spread farther from the focus. The greater the distance from the epicenter, the smaller are the waves and the less is the shaking and damage. The 1906 San Francisco earthquake of magnitude 7.9 was felt from Oregon to Los Angeles, a distance of 700 miles, and 350 miles to the east in Winnemucca. Severe destruction, though, was restricted to the area from Eureka to Santa Cruz; damage was great but not as extensive between Monterey and King City; in the Coalinga area damage was slight; and there was no damage at all south of San Luis Obispo. The isoseismal map shows how shaking and damage diminished in concentric rings outward from the epicenter of the 1892 quake on the Laguna Salada fault. The numbers on the map are Mercalli intensities.

Damage also is related to duration of shaking, which can vary from a few seconds to as much as several minutes. Much more damage is done if shaking is prolonged for more than a few seconds, even though the intensity of shaking is the same. In both the San Francisco (1906) and Alaska (1964) earthquakes, intense shaking continued for at least half a minute.

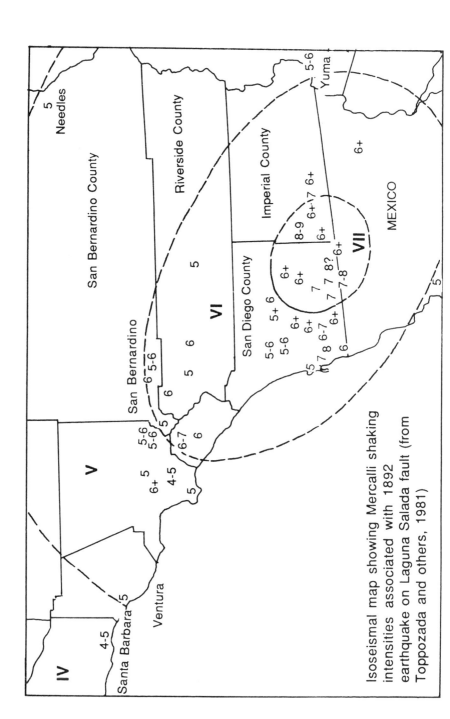

Isoseismal map showing Mercalli shaking intensities associated with 1892 earthquake on Laguna Salada fault (from Toppozada and others, 1981)

24

The amount of shaking and consequent damage in a given place also is strongly influenced by the nature of the ground there. In the 1985 Mexico City earthquake some buildings built on loose, water-filled sands were totally destroyed, while others built on bedrock literally across the street were undisturbed. The epicenter, incidentally, was on the coast some 200 miles away.

The greatest shaking, and consequent damage, occurs on loose, uncondolidated sediments, especially if they are saturated with water. Water-saturated sediments are subject to liquefaction, a process in which shaking turns a coherent mass of wet sediment into jelly, causing the ground to flow and crack and buildings to topple. Unconsolidated sediments on hillsides also are prone to landslides, again especially if they are water-saturated.

Soft or poorly consolidated rocks shake less than loose sediment, and hard, solid rocks are even more stable. Granite, basalt, limestone, and similar rigid bedrock formations are the least subject to earthquake shaking.

Shaking damage to structures also varies dramatically according to type and quality of construction. Rigid structures of masonry, stone, or adobe are more susceptible to shaking damage than are more flexible wooden frame buildings. Unreinforced brick and masonry structures, including walls, chimneys, and building parapets, are especially vulnerable. So are both older wooden frame buildings that are not reinforced or bolted securely to reinforced foundations and newer frame buildings that have large windows or poorly reinforced garages underneath.

While most earthquake destruction results from shaking, surface rupture of faults also can cause considerable damage. If buildings, roads, bridges, aqueducts, pipelines, or other structures are built across faults, ground rupture of those faults can be devastating, although relatively few structures usually are involved.

25

Tsunamis, or seismic sea waves, can be triggered by strong earthquakes beneath the sea, and they pose potential danger to coastal areas. Coastal San Diego County appears, however, not to be highly vulnerable to this hazard, apparently because of the configuration of the coastline relative to the likely sources of such waves. There have been no damaging tsunamis here during historic time.

Among a variety of other hazards associated with earthquakes are ground subsidence, oscillation of water in lakes or rivers (seiches), changes in water table, floods from dam failure, and fires. Generally these and other effects are minor, but they can be disastrous, as shown by the 1906 San Francisco fire.

In addition to the extensive damage that strong earthquakes might cause in homes, businesses, and other private buildings, there may be an equally great threat to the community in the damage that can be done to public structures. These include buildings — such as hospitals, schools, and police and fire facilities — and

Earthquake damage; intensity VII (from photo provided by Rick Miller)

transportation and utility lifelines — airports, highways, railroads, harbors, telephone lines, electric transmission lines, gas pipelines, water supply lines, sewage lines, and dams. The conclusions of a recent study (Reichle and others, 1990; Reichle, 1991) of such effects from a projected earthquake of magnitude 6.8 between San Diego and Tijuana give an idea of what might be expected there, and similar effects could be anticipated throughout the County from earthquakes in other areas. (The hypothesized future earthquake described in chapter II is based on this projection.)

Individuals and business and community leaders should make preparations for their families and communities to be able to go without water, electricity, natural gas, and telephone service for days or even weeks in the event of a major earthquake. They should also be aware that firefighting efforts could be severely hampered during the first 72 hours because of broken water lines and blocked streets, and medical and other emergency aid could be similarly hampered as well as overwhelmed by requests for assistance.

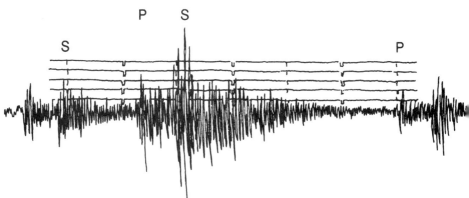

SDSU seismogram for the 1987 Whittier earthquake. Three successive shocks are shown, each with an initial primary wave followed by a larger secondary wave. The 20-second delay between their arrivals (there are 30-second marks on the other lines) is the difference in their travel times from Whittier to San Diego.

# VIII. EARTHQUAKES ARE MEASURED IN MAGNITUDE AND INTENSITY

Seismographs are instruments that record precisely the arrival times of the several different kinds of seismic waves that travel at different velocities from the focus of an earthquake. The lengths of the time intervals between those arrivals indicate the distance to the focus, and distances measured from three different seismograph stations can be used to locate the point of origin by triangulation.

Seismographs also measure the distance that the earth's surface is moved by the passage of seismic waves. The seismograph magnifies the earth movement, and a pen traces out a seismogram like the one on the cover of this book. The greater the magnitude of an earthquake, the larger the waves it dispatches, and the wider the swing of the seismogram line. Operating seismographs can be seen at the Natural History Museum in Balboa Park, in the gift shop museum at Scripps Institution of Oceanography, and in the Department of Geological Sciences at San Diego State University.

There are two kinds of scales for measuring and comparing earthquakes — one of magnitude and one of intensity. The magnitude scale is the one that is based on seismograph measurement of ground vibration and which thus indirectly measures the energy released at the focus of the quake. Best-known and most widely used is the Richter scale. It is based on a logarithmic comparison of the seismograph-measured heights (amplitudes) of earthquake waves. Each step on the scale thus marks a tenfold increase in height of the waves that pass through the ground. The waves in fact represent only a few per cent of the total energy released by an earthquake; a quake of magnitude 8 radiates not just ten, but more than thirty times the energy, therefore, of one of magnitude 7, and it has a thousand times as much seismic energy as one of magnitude 6.

It is a common misconception that the Richter scale extends from one to ten. In fact it has no lower and upper limits. Quakes of very little energy actually have minus magnitude numbers. The smallest quakes detectable by seismographs have magnitudes near -3, while those of magnitude 2.5 to 3.0, of which there are approximately 100,000 annually, are the weakest that can be felt by people in the immediate area. The energy released by the first nuclear bomb explosion was about that of an earthquake of magnitude 5, but severe destruction from earthquakes begins only near magnitude 6. A magnitude 7 quake can be detected around the entire planet, and about 15 to 20 such major shocks occur in an average year.

It has been found that the Richter scale is not accurate for measuring earthquakes stronger than about magnitude 8, and a modified scale has been developed to measure these more powerful quakes. The 1906 San Francisco earthquake has been downgraded to magnitude 7.9 on this scale, while the 1964 Alaska quake has been upgraded to 9.2, the second strongest known earthquake. The strongest of all was a 1960 Chilean quake, which measured 9.5 on the new scale.

The two most powerful earthquakes ever recorded by seismographs were in Colombia and Ecuador in 1906 and in Japan in 1933. Both measured 8.9 on the Richter scale, and each released some three million times the energy of the first nuclear bomb. Magnitude numbers commonly are indicated by a capital M, as in M5 (magnitude five).

The Mercalli scale of earthquake intensity is used to indicate an earthquake's apparent severity at a particular location, and it is based on the observed effects of the shaking produced by the quake. Intensity is determined from damage surveys and from descriptions of shaking effects by people in the area. Intensity of past earthquakes can be estimated from written accounts in newspapers, letters, diaries, and other such  sources.

While magnitude is an indirect measure of energy produced at the focus and has only one value for a given earthquake, intensity decreases with increasing distance from the epicenter and with variations in local geologic conditions. Intensity numbers usually are indicated by two capital M's, as in MM VII (Modified Mercalli intensity of seven). Following is an abbreviated form of the modified Mercalli scale of felt earthquake intensity. More complete descriptions can be found in seismologist Bruce Bolt's (1988) book and in many other sources.

I — Felt only by a very few people under exceptionally favorable circumstances.

II — Felt only by a few people at rest, especially on upper floors. Suspended objects may swing.

III — Felt distinctly indoors, especially on upper floors. Standing vehicles may rock slightly. Vibration like that of a passing truck.

IV — Felt indoors by many but outdoors by few. Some people awakened at night. Standing vehicles rock noticeably. Dishes, windows, and doors disturbed. Walls make cracking sound. Sensation like that of a truck striking the building.

V — Felt by nearly everyone. Many awakened. Trees, buildings, and other tall structures sway. Small objects overturned. Some dishes and windows broken. Some cracked plaster. Pendulum clocks may stop.

VI — Felt by all. Many frightened and run outdoors. Some heavy furniture moved. Some fallen plaster or damaged chimneys. Damage slight.

VII — Everyone runs outdoors. Damage negligible in well-designed and well-built structures; slight to moderate in ordinary well-built structures; considerable in badly designed or poorly built structures. Some chimneys broken. Felt by people in moving vehicles.

VIII — Damage slight in specially designed structures; considerable in ordinary substantial buildings; great in poorly built structures. Panel walls thrown out of frame structures. Chimneys, factory stacks, columns, monuments, and walls toppled. Heavy furniture overturned. Some sand and mud ejected. Changes in well water. Disturbs people in moving vehicles.

IX — Damage considerable in specially designed structures. Well-designed frame structures thrown out of plumb. Buildings shifted off foundations. Ground cracked conspicuously. Underground pipes broken.

X — Some well-built wooden structures and most masonry and frame structures destroyed. Ground badly cracked. Rails bent. Many landslides from river banks and slopes. Shifted sand and mud. Water splashed over banks.

XI — Few if any masonry structures remain standing. Bridges destroyed. Broad fissures in ground. Underground pipelines completely out of service. Earth slumps and landslips in soft ground. Rails bent greatly.

XII — Damage total. Waves seen on ground surfaces. Lines of sight and level distorted. Objects thrown upwards into the air.

The following table shows approximate relationships between earthquake magnitude and intensity at the epicenter. Intensity decreases with increasing distance from the epicenter.

| M | MM |
|---|---|
| 3 | III |
| 4 | IV-V |
| 5 | VI-VII |
| 6 | VII-VIII |
| 7 | IX-X |
| 8 + | XI-XII |

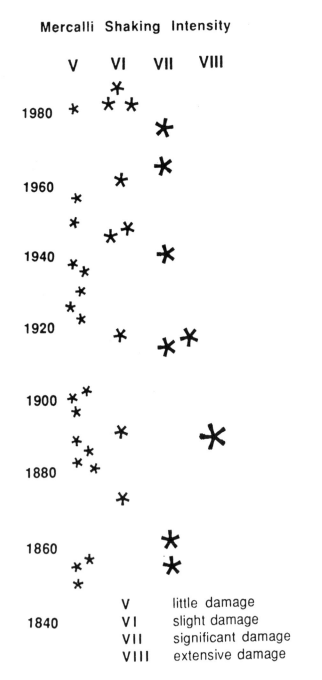

## Mercalli Shaking Intensity

|  | V | VI | VII | VIII |
|---|---|---|---|---|
| V | little damage |
| VI | slight damage |
| VII | significant damage |
| VIII | extensive damage |

# EARTHQUAKE SHAKING IN SAN DIEGO COUNTY

# IX. MANY STRONG EARTHQUAKES HAVE STRUCK SAN DIEGO COUNTY IN THE PAST TWO CENTURIES

The following table lists all the earthquakes that have produced strong shaking or damage in San Diego County since 1800. No records of strong earthquakes are known from before that time. The list has been compiled principally from the two books by Toppozada and others (1981, 1982). The table gives dates, magnitudes (estimated for dates before 1934, when seismographs were first used here), epicenter locations, and intensities and damage from various places in the County. Question marks indicate that magnitude or epicenter location are not known or that information given is uncertain. Notice that many of the earthquakes listed here, especially those of large magnitude, had epicenters outside San Diego County. The fault map in chapter VIII shows epicenters of those quakes of magnitude 4.5 or greater that have struck in or near San Diego County or in the offshore area.

## STRONG EARTHQUAKES IN SAN DIEGO COUNTY

1800  Nov. 22. M6.5? Coastal San Diego County. MM VII at San Diego and San Juan Capistrano; Adobe walls cracked.

1803  May 25. ? ? MM VI at San Diego; mission church damaged slightly. MM VI-VII inland.

1812  Dec. 8. ? San Andreas fault. Strong shaking but no damage at San Diego. San Juan Capistrano Mission church destroyed; 40 killed.

1852  Apr. 12. ? ? MM VII in San Diego. One home destroyed but no other damage.

1852  Nov. 29. ? Mexicali Valley. MM V in San Diego.

1856  Sep. 20. ? San Diego County. MM VII at Santa Ysabel; walls cracked and ceilings fell. MM VI in San Diego; windows rattled and small objects upset.

1857  Jan. 9. M7.9. Fort Tejon. MM V in San Diego; minor damage.

1859  Mar. 25. ? ? MM V at Ballena; cracked ground.

33

1862 May 27. M5.9? Coastal San Diego County. MM VII in San Diego. Buildings and wet ground cracked; door hinges, windows, and crockery broken; pendulum clocks stopped; bell rang at Army Depot. MM V-VI at Temecula and Aguanga; plates rattled and objects upset. Roof shingles cracked at Mesa Grande. Strong at Vallecitos and felt at Anaheim. Many aftershocks into 1863, especially May 29, June 13, and Oct. 21. Strongest quake in San Diego's recorded history.

1875 Nov. 15. ? Imperial Valley. Destroyed buildings in Mexicali. MM VI in Campo; furniture upset and dishes knocked off shelves. MM IV in San Diego; clocks stopped.

1885 Sep. 13. ? ? MM V in San Diego.

1886 Oct. 8. ? ? MM V in San Diego.

1890 Feb. 5. ? ? MM V in San Diego; dishes rattled.

1890 Feb. 9. M6? San Jacinto, Riverside County? MM V throughout San Diego County.

1891 Jul. 30. M7. Colorado River delta. MMVI in Yuma. MM V in San Diego; clocks stopped, china rattled, and furniture moved.

1892 Feb. 23. M6.7-7.3. Northern Baja California. MM VIII-IX in east County; adobe buildings destroyed at Carrizo Stage Station. MM VII at Jacumba, Borrego Springs, Campo (collapsed and cracked walls and goods off shelves), and San Diego (many buildings cracked and chimneys and plaster fallen). MM VI at Julian (light objects upset) and Escondido (objects overturned and goods off shelves). Felt in Visalia and Santa Barbara.

1894 Oct. 23. M5.5-5.7. Mountains east of San Diego. MM VII in mountains. MM V in San Diego; people fled from creaking and cracked buildings, and plaster fell. strong at Escondido.

1899 Jul. 22. M6.5. Cajon Pass. MM V throughout San Diego County.

1899 Dec. 25. M6.6-7.0. San Jacinto, Riverside County. MM VII at Agua Tibia Ranch and Warner Springs. MM VI at Ramona, Escondido, and Jacumba. MM V-VI in San Diego; clocks stopped and glass broken.

1903 Jan. 23. M7. Colorado River delta. MM V in San Diego County.
1906 Apr. 19. M6. Imperial Valley. MM V in San Diego, Ramona, and Julian.
1915 Nov. 20. M7.I. Near Cerro Prieto, Baja California. MM V-VI in San Diego.
1918 Apr. 21. M6.8. Near San Jacinto. MM VII at Warner Springs and Valley Center. MM VI at Fallbrook, Mesa Grande, Julian, Escondido, Oceanside, and San Diego; clocks stopped and small objects upset
1919 Dec. 31. ? ? MM VI at Warner Springs (adobe walls cracked) and Mesa Grande.
1920 Oct. 5. ? ? Trees shaken and everyone ran outdoors at Warner Springs.
1927 Aug. 14. ? Near Barrett Reservoir. MM V+ at Alpine and Jacumba.
1929 Dec. 2. ? Near Ensenada. MM V+ at San Diego.
1934 Dec. 31. M7.1. South of Calexico. MM V-VI in San Diego; buildings cracked, plaster fell, and windows broken. MM IV in Solana Beach, Ramona, and Escondido.
1937 Mar. 25. M6.0. County line north of Borrego Springs.
1939 May I. M5. 60 miles southwest of San Diego. MM V in San Diego.
1940 May 18. M6.7. Imperial fault, Imperial County. MM V in Borrego Springs. MM IV in San Diego.
1942 Oct. 21. M6.5. Near Borrego Valley. MM VII in Carrizo Gorge. MM VI in Warner Springs, Santa Ysabel, Jacumba, and Campo; plaster cracked and glass broken. MM V at Aguanga, Escondido, Mesa Grande, Mount Laguna, and Oceanside.
1949 Nov. 4. M5.7. Baja California. MM VI in San Diego and Campo; large buildings and trees swayed, some buildings cracked, and people ran outdoors.
1951 Dec. 25. M5.9. San Clemente Island. MM VI in San Diego and Del Mar; goods off shelves and plaster cracked. MM V at Mount Laguna, Pala, and Barrett Dam. MM IV at Campo, Escondido, Jamul, Julian, Leucadia, Oceanside, Santa Ysabel.

1954 Mar. 19. M6.2. Santa Rosa Mountains. MM VI in Borrego Springs, Warner Springs, Jamul, and San Diego; plaster cracked and glass broken. MM V in Aguanga, Campo, Julian, Pala, Ramona, Escondido, Del Mar, and Oceanside.

1956 Feb. 9. M6.8. Baja California. MM VI in Campo and San Diego; plaster cracked. MM V in Cardiff, Carlsbad, Del Mar, Poway, Escondido, and Pala.

1958 Jan. 14. M3.7. Chula Vista. MM V in San Diego.

1964 Jun. 21. M3.7. San Diego Bay. MM VI in San Diego; slight damage.

1964 Jun. 22. M3.6. San Diego Bay. MM VI; a typewriter bounced off a table, water splashed in a tub, and fire alarms were activated.

1964 Dec. 22. M5.6. Offshore Ensenada; MM VI in Imperial Beach and San Diego; slight damage.

1968 Apr. 9. M6.5. Ocotillo Wells. MM VII at Borrego Mountain and Ocotillo Wells. MM VI in Borrego Springs, Campo, Julian, Alpine, Ramona, Escondido, Del Mar, and Encinitas. MM V in La Jolla.

1979 Oct. 15. M6.6. Imperial fault, Imperial County. MM VI in San Diego.

1983 Jun. 29. M4.6. l2 miles west of Tijuana. MM V in San Diego.

1984 Jul. 1. M4.3. West of Solana Beach.

1985 Jun. 17. M4.2. San Diego Bay. MM VI in San Diego.

1986 Jul. 13. M5.3. 25 miles west of Solana Beach. MM VI from San Diego to Oceanside; broken windows and waterlines; cracked walls, patios, and sidewalks; fallen tiles; $400,000 damage.

1986 Jul. 3l. M4.1. 25 miles west of Solana Beach.

1986 Oct. 28. M4.7. Southeast San Diego. MM VI in San Diego.

1987 Nov. 23 and 24. M6.2 and 6.6. Superstition Hills, Imperial County. MM VI in Borrego Springs, Warner Springs, Jacumba and Jamul. MM V in Campo, Julian, Ramona, and Escondido.

1988 May 17. M4.2. 8 miles east of Borrego Springs. MM VI in Borrego Springs.

1989 Sep. 4. M3.8. 12 miles northeast of Borrego Springs. MM V in Borrego Springs.

1990 Aug. 5. M4.0. 5 miles north of Warner Springs. MM VI in Warner Springs.

1991 Oct. 13. M3.7. 10 miles north of Lake Henshaw. MM VI at Warner Springs and Pauma Valley.

1991 Dec. 4. M4.2. 10 miles west of Santa Ysabel.

1992 Apr. 22. M6.3. West end of Joshua Tree National Monument, 11 miles east of Desert Hot Springs.

1992 Jun. 28. M7.5. Landers, San Bernardino County. MM VI in coastal San Diego; water pipes broken, plaster and concrete walls cracked, power lost to 6000 homes and businesses. MM V in Borrego Springs (airport lost power), Aguanga, Warner Springs, Escondido. MM IV in Julian, Vista, Oceanside, Santee.

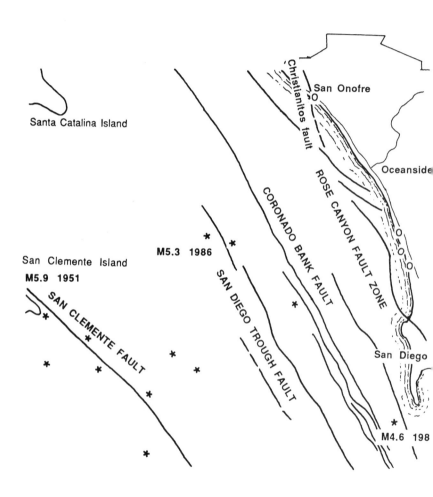

Map of San Diego County and offshore area showing active faults (labeled), earthquake epicenters (stars) from chapter IX, and fault localities described in chapter X.

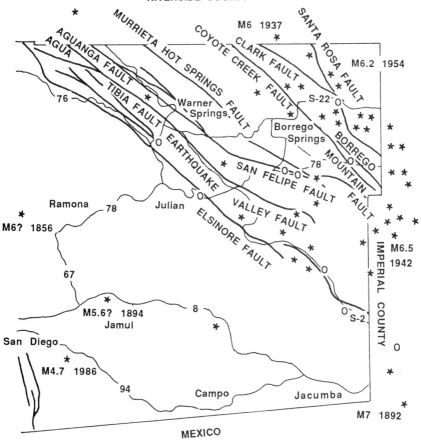

# X. SAN DIEGO COUNTY'S MANY ACTIVE FAULTS CAN BE EASILY SEEN, AND MAGNITUDES OF THEIR FUTURE EARTHQUAKES CAN BE ESTIMATED

## INTRODUCTION

The map on the preceding pages shows the major active faults and fault zones and epicenters of strong historic earthquakes in San Diego County and offshore as far as San Clemente Island. Though locations are approximate, especially for quakes that occurred before 1934, notice that the epicenters are concentrated in the fault zones.

Three kinds of information are presented in the text for each of these faults. There is a description of each zone, together with information on and illustrations of locations where it can be easily seen. This part of the text can serve as a field guide to San Diego County's active faults. There is also an account of each fault's earthquake history and of what is known about slip rates, recurrence intervals , and other seismic characteristics. Finally there is a discussion of future earthquake potential, as best it can be estimated from historic records and from geologic evidence.

These estimates of future earthquake potential are taken from the most recent technical publications on the subject. The principal sources, with full references given in the Bibliography, are McEuen and Pinckney (l972), Leighton and Associates (1983), Wesnousky (1986), Woodward-Clyde Consultants (1986), and Anderson, Agnew, and Rockwell (1989). A more complete and more technical discussion can be found in my report to the County Office of Disaster Preparedness (Kern, 1987). The estimates of future earthquake magnitude and shaking intensity are summarized in chapter XI.

## OFFSHORE FAULTS

**Fault descriptions.** The continental borderland west of San Diego is crossed by a complex system of faults that are continuous with onshore faults in northern Baja California and in coastalmost southern California. Both offshore and onshore parts of this system pose potential earthquake hazards to San Diego County. The major faults offshore are the Coronado Bank, San Diego Trough, and San Clemente. The Coronado Bank fault is continuous to the north with the Palos Verdes Hills fault and to the south with the Agua Blanca fault south of Ensenada. The latter also branches northward to connect with the San Diego Trough fault. The San Clemente fault comes ashore farther south as the San Isidro fault zone.

The Agua Blanca fault zone comes ashore at Punta Banda, on the south edge of Bahia de Todos Santos at Ensenada. The Point itself extends seaward as a fault block within the zone and is bracketed by the Agua Blanca fault itself on the north and the Maximinos fault on the south. Though several north-south faults within the zone are exposed on the north shore of Punta Banda, the Agua Blanca fault lies just offshore and passes under the south end of the estuary. Inland the fault zone follows Punta Banda Ridge into Valle Santo Tomas and Valle Agua Blanca, but nowhere are there clear exposures where the fault can be easily seen.

**Earthquake history.** Recent activity is indicated on all three of the offshore fault zones by ocean-floor scarps, offset submarine canyons, and offsets of uppermost ocean-floor sediments. Recent seismicity also clearly delineates these faults and further attests to their activity. On land the San Miguel fault is active along its entire length and appears to be the seismically dominant zone in northern Baja California. It has produced several earthquakes of magnitude 6.0 to 6.8. No moderate or large-magnitude historical earthquake can be readily associated with the Agua Blanca fault, but earthquakes of magnitude 3 to 5 have occurred along its offshore portion. The Coronado Bank fault zone also is characterized by a linear trend of magnitude 3 to 5 earthquakes offshore from San Diego. The July, 1986, quake of magnitude 5.3 was centered within the northern portion of the Coronado Bank fault zone west of Del Mar. The San Clemente fault zone also has high seismicity; the largest historic earthquake in that zone was magnitude 5.9 in 1951.

The only two earthquakes known to have caused significant damage in the coastal zone were those of 1800 and 1862. Intensity VII shaking associated with the 1800 quake is indicated by reports of cracked adobe walls both at San Diego and San Juan Capistrano. It is estimated that the quake must have had a magnitude of at least 6.5 to have caused such damage in both places. There are not enough records to locate an epicenter, but it presumably was in the coastal zone near or between the two missions. The epicenter of the 1862 quake must have been in or just west of San Diego, probably in either the Rose Canyon or Coronado Bank fault zones. Magnitude is estimated at about 6, and intensity of VII is indicated by damage reports at two locations in San Diego.

With these two exceptions earthquake activity had been low in the coastal zone during the past 200 years and especially during this century. From 1932 to 1982 the largest quake in the immediate vicinity of San Diego was one of magnitude 3.7 in 1964. Between 1983 and 1986, however, coastal San Diego County was struck by earthquakes of magnitude 4.6 (June 29, 1983), 4.3 (July 1, 1984), 4.0 (June 17, 1985), and 5.3 (July 13, 1986). Some 40 quakes of magnitude 3.5 or greater struck the broader San Diego area from 1984 through 1986, matching the number between 1944 and 1984. These events, of course, marked just the beginning of the past decade's increase in earthquake activity, as described in chapter I.

**Future earthquake estimates.** On land the northwestern l2- to l8-mile segment of the Agua Blanca

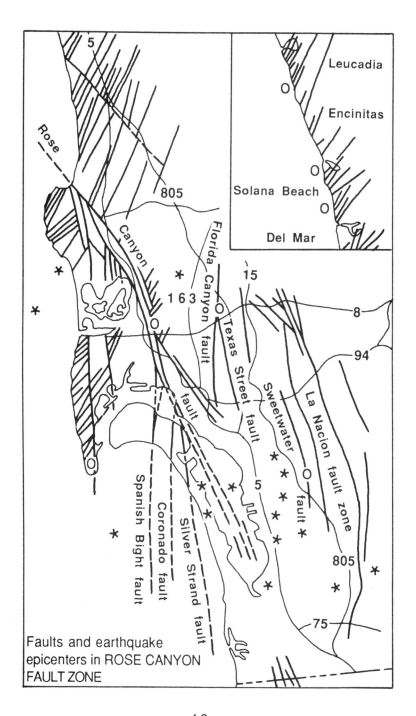

Faults and earthquake
epicenters in ROSE CANYON
FAULT ZONE

Labels within figure:
- 5
- Rose
- 805
- Canyon
- Florida Canyon fault
- Leucadia
- Encinitas
- Solana Beach
- Del Mar
- 15
- 1 6 3
- Texas Street fault
- 8
- 94
- Sweetwater fault
- La Nacion fault zone
- fault
- 5
- Spanish Bight fault
- Coronado fault
- Silver Strand fault
- 805
- 75

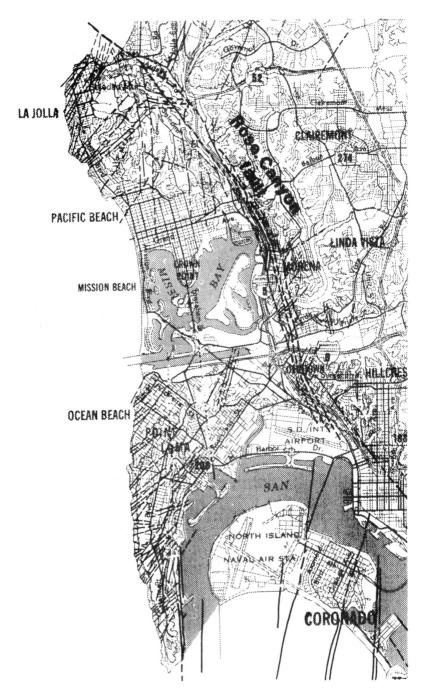

ROSE CANYON FAULT ZONE. Thinner lines are inactive faults along the coast north and south of La Jolla Shores; heavier lines are active or possibly active strands of the Rose Canyon fault.

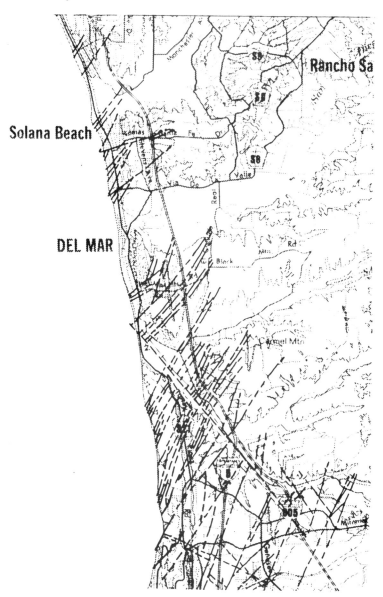

fault is thought to be capable of an earthquake of M6.7 to 7.2 (Anderson, Agnew, and Rockwell, 1989). The average recurrence interval for such quakes would be about 125 to 250 years.

Leighton and Associates (1983) estimated a maximum probable earthquake on the Coronado Bank fault of magnitude 5.8 to 6.2, with a recurrence interval of 100 to 200 years. Woodward-Clyde Consultants (1986) suggested a magnitude range of 6.2 to 7.2, while Anderson, Agnew, and Rockwell (1989) estimated a maximum plausible magnitude range of 6.1 to 7.7 for earthquakes rupturing multiple segments of this fault.

The maximum earthquake range for the San Diego Trough fault has been estimated at magnitude 6.2 to 6.7 (Woodward-Clyde Consultants, 1986) and 6.1 to 7.7 (Anderson, Agnew, and Rockwell, 1989).

The poorly known San Clemente fault is thought to be capable of earthquakes up to magnitude 7.7 (Woodward-Clyde Consultants, 1986; Anderson, Agnew, and Rockwell, 1989).

## ROSE CANYON FAULT ZONE

**Fault descriptions — Rose Canyon fault**. Dominant among the County's onshore coastal faults is the one in Rose Canyon. On the preceding pages you will find three maps of the Rose Canyon fault zone. The generalized map of the entire zone is followed by two detailed views of most of the metropolitan area. These more detailed maps have been taken from the County-wide fault map that I compiled for the 1987 report for the County Office of Disaster Preparedness. (Unfortunately, this report is now out of print.) On these detailed maps the clearly inactive northeast-trending faults are shown by thinner lines than the active, or possibly active, through-going faults.

The Rose Canyon fault crosses San Diego from south-southeast to north-northwest, passing from San Diego Bay along the east shore of Mission Bay, through Rose Canyon, and out to sea at La Jolla Shores. It extends beneath the sea at least 25 miles northward to the sea floor west of Oceanside, and it may continue on to connect with the Newport-Inglewood fault — site of the 1933 Long Beach earthquake. It is parallel to the San Andreas and other major faults of the southern California region, and rocks west of the Rose Canyon fault are similarly plowing northward past rocks on its eastern side. Sandstones of the San Diego Formation, for example, are found high on the south flank of Mount Soledad west of the fault but are restricted on its east side to the south wall of Mission Valley. Though it apparently is much less active and powerful than its notorious relatives, these features reveal the Rose Canyon fault as a member of that zone of fractures that mark the boundary between the Pacific and American plates.

Mount Soledad and south La Jolla thus are slipping seaward past La Jolla Shores, while Point Loma follows them past downtown San Diego. The illustration shows where the bend in the fault at Ardath Road has further caused the western block to ride upward there. Mount Soledad has

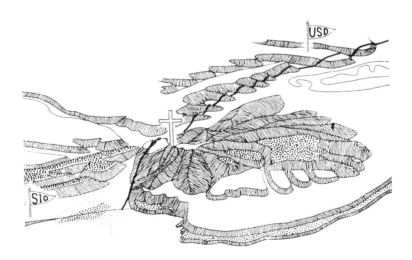

Mount Soledad

thus been raised hundreds of feet above the mesa, and Rose Canyon has been deflected southward and become deeply incised behind the intruding mountain. The main fault strand crosses the steep slopes south of Ardath Road, where the uplifted block towers over its neighbor to the east and north. Farther south, on the other hand, Mission Bay and San Diego Bay have subsided below the level of the mesa east of that stretch of the fault, which traverses the steep slope above those shores. These relationships can be seen on a clear day from the Easter Cross on Mount Soledad. The fault's continued southward course is uncertain where covered by the city and the water, and the zone appears to die out under San Diego Bay, with its motions passing on to the offshore faults to the west.

Rocks and faults are poorly exposed in San Diego because they are covered by streets, parking lots, buildings, lawns, and shrubbery. In spite of its prominence, therefore, the Rose Canyon fault is not easily seen. One of its several strands, however, is exposed behind the left-center-field fence of the Pony League baseball diamond in Tecolote Park's south corner. Half-million-year-old

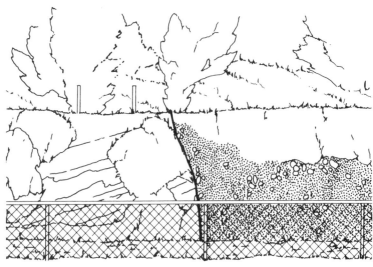

ROSE CANYON FAULT in Tecolote Park

(Pleistocene) conglomerate is on the right side of this fault, with light-colored 50 million-year-old (Eocene) sandstone of the Scripps Formation to the left. Incidentally, this exposure will be part of an earthquake hazard exhibit in the visitor center that now has been rescheduled for completion in March, 1994, in Tecolote Canyon Natural Reserve. This exhibit will include the Rose Canyon fault model described in chapter XI.

The youngest features that are known to have been dismembered by the Rose Canyon fault, and the ones incidentally that most clearly reveal its nature, are a series of Pleistocene marine terraces at La Jolla Bay. These are flat benches, like the one exposed by low tides at Bird Rock or the tip of Point Loma. They are carved by the sea and may later be lifted above the shore where the crust is buckled upward by folds or faults. For example, the grassy surface of the park at La Jolla Cove (fine stipple in the illustration) and the higher surface under downtown La Jolla have been pushed respectively 80 feet and 200 feet upward above their subterranean levels beneath La Jolla Shores on the other side of the Rose Canyon fault. Those terraces are only about 105,000 and 120,000 years old, so the fault has been busy here in that short span of time. Another terrace that is more than half a million years old has become even more disjointed because of the fault. It is conspicuous in the Mount Soledad illustration (coarser stipple) at elevations of 340 feet north and east of Ardath Road and 625 feet across the Rose Canyon fault on Mount Soledad.

The three San Diego fault maps show that nearly all other large-scale fractures in the city diverge from the Rose Canyon fault like the branches of a tree, each extending only a short distance before dying out. Most of these branches, however, are oriented at clockwise angles of approximately 30 to the trunk, so those east of the main fault extend toward the north while those on its western side reach to the south. This distinctive pattern is characteristic of fault zones, like the San Andreas and its partners in the southern California region, along which

49

rocks viewed across the trunk fault have moved to the right.  The specific term "right-slip fault" is used by geologists to distinguish this category of faults.

None of the many faults in this extensive branching system are active.  This is clear from the fact that none of them cut the 105,000- and 120,000-year-old terraces.  It is also characteristic of right-slip (and left-slip) fault zones that they originate as extensive sets of faults crossing the zone and that those faults become inactive when the main fault itself later develops.  Many of the branch faults are normal faults, in which the fracture plane is sloping and the overhanging block has slipped down relative to the underlying one.  This relationship can be seen in the illustration of the Florida Canyon fault, as well as in several subsequent illustrations.

Following are brief accounts of several of the  principal faults that branch from the Rose Canyon.

**Florida Canyon fault.** In spite of generally poor exposure of rocks in San Diego, many of the principal secondary faults, or at least their topographic effects, can be seen.  A good example is the Florida Canyon fault, which achieved some notoriety because of its proximity to the Naval Hospital in Balboa Park.  Adams Avenue, El Cajon Boulevard, University Avenue, Morley Field Drive, and Zoo Place all plunge steeply just east of Park Boulevard.  That abrupt descent marks the fault scarp — the eroded face of the uplifted block — where the mesa surface east of the fault has subsided as much as 65 feet below its level to the west.  The illustration shows this topographic relationship, as well as the corresponding displacement of red terrace sandstones that blanket the mesa.  Florida Canyon has been carved into the gently sloping mesa by the eroding action of surface water that begins flowing seaward but is trapped behind the uplifted block and diverted toward the south.  Even this terrace is less than one million years old, showing that the Florida Canyon fault has been active within that interval.

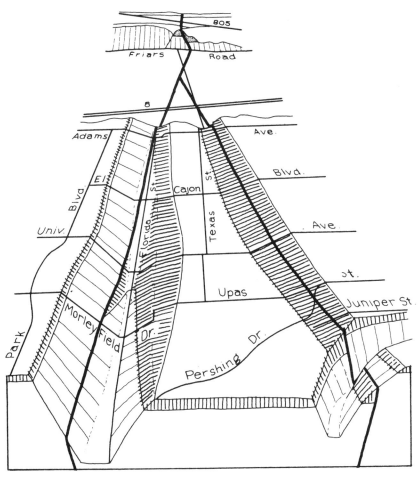

FLORIDA CANYON (left) and TEXAS STREET FAULTS

FLORIDA CANYON FAULT at Friars Road

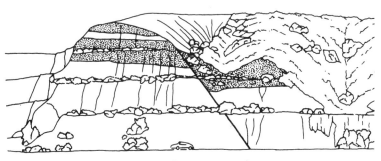

51

The best exposure of the Florida Canyon fault is in the cut bank along Friars Road just east of the Conrock quarry and Stadium Way. Partially obscured by brush at the eastern end of the high road cut, the fault plane slopes down toward the right. A dark brown zone (stippled in the illustration) within the Stadium Conglomerate can be seen to be faulted down to a lower level in the overhanging eastern block. Parking is not possible on Friars Road, so this exposure is best seen from Stadium Way and also from the Adams Avenue bridge over Texas Street.

**Texas Street fault.** The terrace that is cut by the Florida Canyon fault is broken by three other faults on San Diego Mesa. Though the fault plane itself is nowhere clearly visible, the Texas Street fault is conspicuous by its topographic expression. As shown in the drawing one can climb its scarp by traveling eastward from Texas Street on Adams Avenue, El Cajon Boulevard, or University Avenue. On Upas Street the scarp is at Pershing Avenue, and it forms the steep slope along Pershing Drive at the northeast corner of Balboa Park and on Juniper and Grape streets east of the Park.

**Fortieth Street fault.** The Fortieth Street fault is like the one in Florida Canyon in sloping eastward and having the west side higher. Though its surface expression is not so evident to the traveler of city streets, westward-flowing surface water has similarly been diverted to north and south, carving small canyons that descend in those directions, as along Ward Road.

**La Nacion fault.** The several strands of the La Nacion fault system mimic the geometry of the Texas Street fault. They slope in most places toward the west, and the mesa surface is lower in that direction. In this case, in fact, it drops down in several steps which one ascends in traveling eastward along El Cajon Boulevard from Euclid Avenue past 54th Street. As at Florida Canyon and Texas Street these faults cut the veneer of red terrace sandstone that covers the mesa.

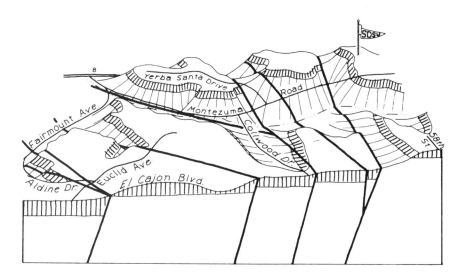

LA NACION FAULT ZONE

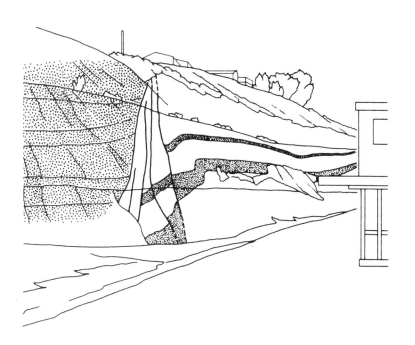

SWEETWATER FAULT at Twin Hills Youth Park

The La Nacion fault zone extends in a broad swath from this area southward through National City and Chula Vista to the Mexican border, and it is exposed in many places.  National City has one outstanding exposure in the northern bluff overlooking Twin Hills Youth Park on Calle Abajo near Valley Road and Sweetwater Road.  The illustration shows how red-brown Pleistocene sandstone and conglomerate in the overhanging block have dropped down at least 50 feet on the left side of the Sweetwater fault to abut against lighter-colored sandstone of the several-million-year-old (Pliocene) San Diego Formation.

**Faults on Point Loma**. Another series of prominent secondary faults branches from the Rose Canyon zone toward the south and southwest.  Those under San Diego Bay and the ocean west of Silver Strand were detected from the echoes that offset beds reflect back to oceanographic research ships from sound waves they have transmitted. Associated faults on land are not clearly exposed, but several of them are topographically conspicuous.  The valley occupied by Nimitz Boulevard, for example, has been eroded along a fault that pushed up the high area on its eastern side.  That small plateau also is bounded on its northwestern edge by another fault that produced the steep bluffs along Worden Street.

The Point Loma peninsula itself apparently exists because of uplift north of faults that parallel Rosecrans Street and west of others that follow the Point's lower eastern shore. A prominent fault in the latter zone cuts through approximately 70 million-year-old (Cretaceous) sandstones of the Cabrillo Formation.  It can be seen near the eastern end of the high sea cliff at the extreme southern end of the Point, but a more accessible if slightly less clear exposure is in the north wall of the first canyon entered by the Bayside Trail in Cabrillo National Monument.  At the latter site a shaly bed is conspicuously lower on the bay side of the fault.

ROSE CANYON FAULT ZONE. Fault on Bayside Trail, Cabrillo National Monument, San Diego

**Faults near Mission Bay.** Several less-prominent, unnamed faults also can be seen clearly in readily accessible exposures. One of these is in the high cut on the east side of Soledad Mountain Road just north of the traffic light at the end of Beryl Street. (This is a busy street; watch for traffic here.) Red and gray sandstones of a Pleistocene terrace deposit (stippled in the illustration) in the overhanging block on the left are bent slightly where faulted down against tan and gray Pliocene sandstone of the San Diego Formation. Above the Pliocene beds the Pleistocene rocks are hidden beneath the houses at the top

ROSE CANYON FAULT ZONE. Fault on Soledad Mountain Road, San Diego

ROSE CANYON FAULT ZONE. Fault on Marion Way, San Diego

of the hill, where they have been heaved 45 feet above their level on the other side of the fault.

Another, lesser branch fault is exposed in the bank along the western entrance road (Marion Way) to the University of San Diego, near the upper end of the bend halfway up the hill. Here brown conglomerate of a Pleistocene terrace deposit (stippled in the illustration) in the overhanging block on the left has been faulted down against tan Eocene sandstone of the Scripps Formation. Above the Eocene rocks the same Pleistocene beds lie 50 feet higher at the top of the hill. The terraces offset by both of the preceding faults are intermediate in age, perhaps as young as one-half million years, so the age of faulting here must be at least that young.

**Faults from Del Mar to Oceanside.** Many of the presumably inactive northeast-trending faults of the Rose Canyon zone can be seen along the coast, especially in sea cliff exposures, from Del Mar to beyond Oceanside. There are fine fault outcrops in the bluffs south of Flat Rock in Torrey Pines Park, where the Rose canyon fault lies just offshore. Exposures are poor from Torrey Pines through Del Mar, but the coastal bluffs from south Solana Beach all the way to San Elijo Lagoon are sliced by faults in many

ROSE CANYON FAULT ZONE. Faults in sea cliffs south of Via de la Valle, Solana Beach

ROSE CANYON FAULT ZONE. Faults in sea cliffs at Cardiff State Beach, Solana Beach

ROSE CANYON FAULT ZONE. Faults in sea cliffs at Leucadia State Beach, Leucadia

places. There are especially good exposures on the beach just south of Via de la Valle and south of the parking lot at Cardiff State Beach at the north end of Solana Beach. In both these places many faults can be clearly seen to cut through the bedrock sandstones but not through the overlying soft terrace sands, showing that these faults have not been active during the past 120,000 years.

For several miles north of San Elijo Lagoon exposures also are poor, but faults can be seen at several places in Leucadia. They are sparse at Moonlight State Beach, but there is a small cluster just beyond the stairs 200 yards south of the parking lot. A better place is below the parking lot at Leucadia State Beach at the foot of Leucadia Boulevard, where faults cut the sandstones and shales both north and south of the base of the beach path.

North of Leucadia the Rose Canyon fault is farther offshore, and few of the northeast-trending faults reach the coast. A prominent exception is the Christianitos fault, which can

CHRISTIANITOS FAULT, San Onofre State Beach

be seen in the sea cliffs at San Onofre State Beach, one mile south of the San Onofre Nuclear Generating Station. This fault, which was of great concern in the siting of the power plant there, appears to be another of the northeast-trending faults of the Rose Canyon zone. It diverges in a clockwise direction from the offshore fault zones, and its failure to cut the young terraces shows it to have been inactive for the past 125,000 years.

**Earthquake history.** The historic earthquake record of the Rose Canyon fault zone is ambiguous because of the uncertainty of epicentral locations of the 1800 and 1862 quakes. Both produced intensities of VI to VII in San Diego and probably were located either on the Rose Canyon fault (with magnitudes of approximately 6.5 and 6.0) or on the Coronado Bank fault. The left bend in the Rose Canyon fault north of Mount Soledad may be locking the fault, perhaps accounting for its low seismic profile during the past century or more. The general lack of earthquake activity in the coastal zone during the past two centureies was broken onshore as well as offshore in the 1980's, as the June 17, 1985, (3.9, 4.0, 3.9) and October 28, 1986, (4.7) quakes were centered under the city.

**Future earthquake estimates.** As information accumulated during the 1980's and early '90's, earthquake risk associated with the Rose Canyon zone received increasing attention. For example, an evaluation of San Diego's seismic sources, which was done as part of a liquefaction study by Woodward-Clyde Consultants (1986), suggested maximum magnitude ranges of 6.2 to 7.2 for the Rose Canyon fault and 6.2 for the La Nacion fault. Other faults in the zone from the La Nacion to east Point Loma also may be active and can be expected to be at least comparable. Wesnousky (1986) estimated expected earthquakes of magnitude 7.1 on the Rose Canyon fault (30-mile segment length) and 6.6 on the La Nacion fault.

Anderson, Agnew, and Rockwell (1989) evaluated seismic potential according to probable rupture length of eight different segments of the Rose Canyon fault. Rupture of the entire well-documented 35-mile length of the fault from Oceanside to San Diego Bay would produce a maximum plausible earthquake of magnitude 6.9. Magnitude 6.4 to 6.6 quakes would result from partial ruptures from La Jolla either to Oceanside or through San Diego Bay. The 40-mile segment off Camp Pendleton could be capable of a quake of magnitude 7.0. In addition, the 12-mile-long La Nacion fault is suggested to be capable of a magnitude 6.5 earthquake, and the same presumably is true of any of the other faults across that zone from there to Point Loma.

More definitive evidence has recently been brought to light in a series of studies by Tom Rockwell and his co-workers (Lindvall and others, 1989; Rockwell and others, 1990, 1991) . In 1989 and again in 1990 they excavated trenches across the fault at the SDG&E Center on Damon Avenue at the mouth of Rose Canyon. Fault features exposed in these trenches have finally shown conclusively that the Rose Canyon fault is active. On page 9's illustration of the vertical wall of the first trench, layer C was shown by carbon dating to be between 8300 and 7870 years old. These dates on this faulted bed provide the first proof that the Rose Canyon fault is active, as it has clearly moved during the past 10,000 years. Other features in the two trenches further reveal that multiple earthquakes have occurred here during the past 6000 to 9000 years, and several of those quakes produced surface rupture, suggesting earthquake magnitudes of 6 or greater.

Excavation of a series of intersecting trenches in 1990 involved the piecemeal removal by hand of some 100 cubic yards of material. This feat was performed in order to expose and trace the entire course of a conspicuous gravel-filled channel in otherwise fine-grained floodplain deposits of silty to clayey sand, as shown in this map-view illustration of the trench exposure (from Rockwell and others, 1991). The channel, which was oriented at right angles to the fault zone, was found to be cut by six separate fault strands and to have a total offset of at least 8.7 meters. This is a minimum figure, as the channel is not

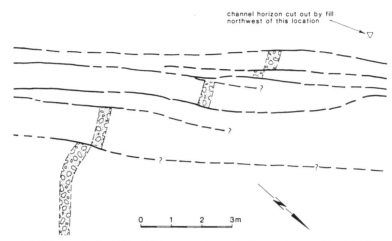

0   1   2   3m

**ROSE CANYON FAULT,** map view of offset channel in 1990
trench exposure

preserved in the westernmost block, where it was
destroyed by excavation in 1960.

Carbon-dating of charcoal — burned wood fragments that
were deposited in the floodplain muds underlying the
channel — has yielded a maximum age of approximately
8155 years (Rockwell and others, 1991).  Fault
movement of at least 8.7 meters in no more than 8155
years indicates a minimum rate of fault slip of
approximately 1.07 mm per year.  If the channel is
significantly younger than the underlying charcoal, and if
the western strand of the fault has greater than the
minimum amount of slip, then the rate could be as high as
2 mm per year.  This figure is the maximum suggested by
offset of the youngest nearby stream terraces.  As there
may also be slip on other strands of the fault to east and
west of the trench area, the suggested overall rate of
movement for the Rose Canyon fault here is between 1.1
and 2.05 mm per year.

This rate, considered in conjunction with the lengths of
fault segments, suggests that the Rose Canyon fault can be
expected to produce earthquakes of magnitude 6 to 7
(Rockwell and others, 1991).  Magnitude-7 quakes would

occur on average every thousand years of so, while quakes of magnitude 6.5 could be expected to recur at approximately 500-year intervals.

In light of this demonstration of the genuine earthquake hazard posed by the Rose Canyon fault, increasing numbers of geologists and engineers have been urging that San Diego be reclassified from zone 3 to zone 4, which signifies the greatest earthquake hazard, in the Uniform Building Code. While the high costs of renovating the 700-odd large masonry buildings that do not meet the earthquake safety construction standards for zone 4 have for the present discouraged this reclassification, it is very likely to be accomplished in time to be included in the 1994 edition of the Code.

Finally, according to California Division of Mines and Geology seismologist Michael Reichle, a magnitude 6.5 earthquake on the Rose Canyon fault could produce shaking intensities as high as MM VIII or IX in San Diego valleys and along bays. Earthquakes in the ranges given above for any of the onshore or nearshore San Diego faults could subject the coastal zone to shaking intensities of VII (at epicenter of magnitude 6 earthquakes ) or even as high as IX to X (at epicenter of magnitude 7 quakes).

## ELSINORE FAULT ZONE

**Fault descriptions**. The Elsinore fault zone crosses eastern San Diego County on its 120-mile path from Los Angeles County to the Mexican border. In addition to the map at the beginning of this chapter, two excerpts from my 1987 compilation for the office of Disaster Preparedness show in more detail the course of the fault along the southwest shore of Lake Henshaw and through Banner. These maps also show the Agua Tibia fault crossing the northeast shore of Lake Henshaw and the San Felipe and Aguanga faults passing respectively northeast of Warner Springs and through Ranchita. From Lake Elsinore it passes near Temecula and up Wolf Valley to enter San Diego County where S-16 crosses the crest north of Pala. The

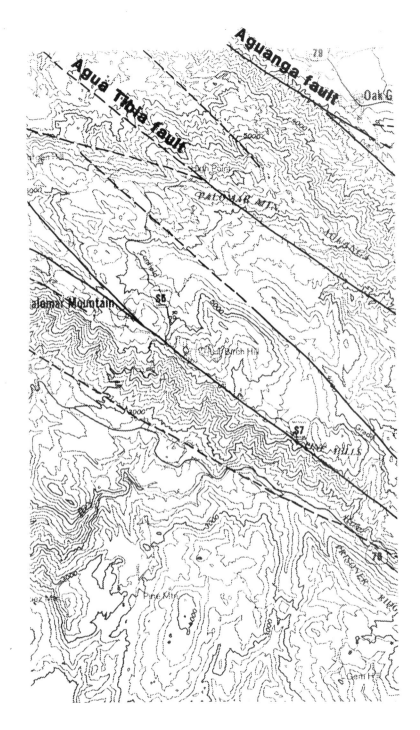

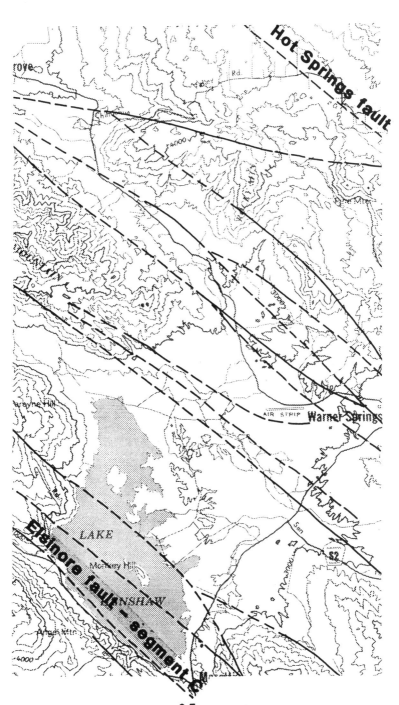

base of the steep southwestern flank of the Agua Tibia-Palomar Mountain ridge marks the passage of the fault toward Lake Henshaw. The alignment of the lake's straight southwestern shoreline with the narrow, steep-walled valleys occupied by route 76 northward from the lake and route 79 to the south reveal the fault's path here. Two separate parallel strands of the fault cross the lake itself, and one of them can be seen in a road-cut exposure on route 79 a half mile northeast of the junction with 76 at the south end of the lake. (I recommend this exposure with reluctance. The cut is narrow and traffic is fast here; park well off the road southwest of the cut and keep out of the way of traffic.) Recent activity on this fault is shown by its cutting of these Pleistocene beds, at most a few million years old.

Three to four miles down routh 79 toward Santa Ysabel the road bends abruptly to the right. Here the fault diverges left from the road and continues straight on up the linear

ELSINORE FAULT on northwest side of route 79 southeast of Lake Henshaw

ELSINORE FAULT on Banner Grade

valley that can be seen to the southeast beyond the bend. It
then goes over a pass above the apple orchards on Farmers
Road north of Julian and continues on down Banner Grade.
On a road map the fault's path can be seen in the alignment
of Banner Grade, routes 76 and 79 near Lake Henshaw, and
the northern few miles of S-16.

There are excellent views of the Elsinore fault from any of
several turnouts on Banner Grade between about 1.5 and 3
miles above the Banner Store. (Park well off the road on
the canyon side and watch for traffic.) From these
turnouts one can look across the canyon to where the fault
line is marked by several distinct benches, by lines of
taller vegetation where water comes up along the fault, and
by steeper slopes (fault scarps) in the lower end of the
canyon. From directly across the canyon the two most
prominent benches can be seen to be the displaced lower
ends of ridges, which have moved to the left (northward)
on the near side of the fault. The gullies between these
ridges also can be seen to have been displaced to the left by
movement on the fault.

From Banner the fault continues southeastward up the straight canyon and on over the saddle west of Granite Mountain. From there it descends into the next valley and crosses County Road S-2 in the bend at the base of the grade. The patchwork of dark and light rocks on the slopes north of the Butterfield Ranch is the result of faulting there. The fault zone crosses the road again into the valley south of the Vallecito Stage Station, then bends left over the ridge to Agua Caliente Springs. This bend marks the boundary between two of the major segments of the fault zone.

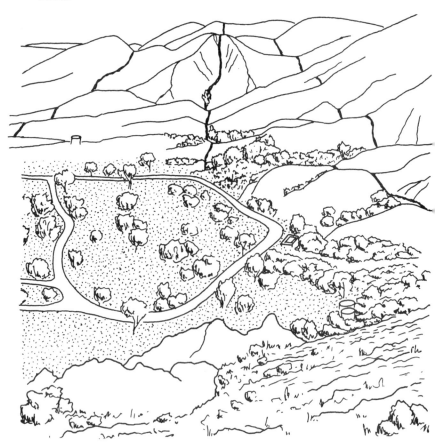

ELSINORE FAULT seen from Desert View Overlook at Agua Caliente Springs

The hot springs at both Vallecito and Agua Caliente result from hot water moving upward through the fractured rocks in the fault zone. At Agua Caliente there are wide zones of crushed rock produced by grinding along the fault. Much of the crushed zone is filled with clay produced by rapid decomposition of feldspars in the granitic rocks partly because of the presence of the hot water. The zone of faulting and crushing is some hundred yards wide at Agua Caliente. Several principal strands are shown in the illustration, and at the base of the slope in the foreground are pinnacles of crushed and clay-seamed rock.

Southeastward from Agua Caliente the fault follows the base of the Tierra Blanca Mountains west of the road, and water in the Mountain Palm Springs area flows up along the fault plane. The fault zone crosses the road again in Carrizo Wash and continues on toward Imperial County along the base of the southwestern flank of the Coyote Mountains. Deformation caused by the Elsinore and some northeast-trending branch faults is clearly visible at the head of Canyon Sin Nombre, and it can be seen even from the overlook road just off S-2 southeast of Sweeney Pass and about four miles from the County line.

ELSINORE FAULT from overlook at Canyon Sin Nombre, north of Ocotillo. Fault crosses view at base of slope

A mosaic of colored rocks along the whole length of the Coyote Mountains reveals the intense faulting that has occurred there, and the Elsinore fault follows the base of the slope all the way to Ocotillo, where it passes on under the sandy desert floor. There are excellent views of the fault at the mouth of Fossil Canyon, which can be reached by a short gravel road directly north of Ocotillo.

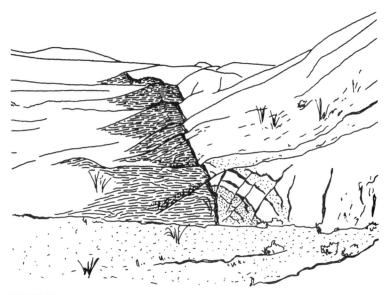

ELSINORE FAULT ZONE at mouth of Fossil Canyon

**Earthquake history and future earthquake estimates.** The maximum probable earthquake for the Elsinore fault zone as a whole has been estimated at magnitude 6.9 to 7.3, with a recurrence interval of 60 years (McEuen and Pinckney, 1972; Woodward-Clyde Consultants, 1986). Recent and on-going studies also have suggested characteristic earthquakes for individual fault segments in the range of magnitude 6 to 7, as described below.

The northwesternmost of four segments (segment A) extends approximately 45 miles from Whittier, in Los Angeles County, to the prominent right step at Lake Elsinore, in Riverside County. The 1910 magnitude 6 earthquake in Temescal Valley occurred on this segment and caused intensity V to VI shaking in northern San Diego County. Wesnousky (1986) suggested an expected earthquake magnitude here of 7.3. Trench studies on this segment have revealed the occurrence of five earthquakes during the past few thousand years. The maximum ground-breaking earthquake recurrence interval of 250 years, combined with a moderate estimated slip rate of 4 to 7 millimeters per year, suggests that the characteristic quake on this segment is magnitude 6 to 7.

The next segment to the southwest (segment B) extends some 30 miles from Elsinore to the sharp bend at Pauma Valley in northern San Diego County. Lack of major historical earthquakes on this segment, combined with a significant slip rate, suggests that  magnitude 7 earthquakes may be characteristic here. Anderson, Agnew, and Rockwell (1989) suggested that the maximum plausible earthquake on this segment is magnitude 6.8, and Wesnousky (1986) gave magnitude 7.1 as the maximum expected quake.

The third segment toward the southeast (segment C) extends some 40 miles from Pauma Valley to the prominent bend at Vallecito. Though no data on earthquake history have yet been obtained in this segment, Anderson, Agnew, and Rockwell (1989) used segment length to estimate a slip rate of 5 to 6 millimeters per year and a maximum expected earthquake of magnitude 7.1. Wesnousky (1986) suggested an expected earthquake magnitude of 7.2.

The southeasternmost segment (segment D) of the Elsinore fault itself extends the last 40 miles to the Mexican border south of Plaster City. Measurements of offset stream channels reveal the occurrence of six prehistoric earthquakes. The amount of horizontal slip per quake ranges from 3 to 6 feet, suggesting magnitude 6.5 to 7 quakes. A recurrence interval of about 350 years has been estimated for these displacements, with the last one being prehistoric. Anderson, Agnew, and Rockwell (1989) estimated a moderate slip rate of 3.5 to 5.5 millimeters per year and an expected quake of magnitude 7, and Wesnousky (1986) suggested a maximum magnitude of 7.2.

The final segment in this fault zone is the Laguna Salada fault, which extends 35 miles beyond the Mexican border. The last earthquake, probably the historic magnitude 6.7 to 7.3 quake in 1892, produced vertical scarps up to 12 feet high (see chapter I) and ruptured for a length of at least 12 miles. Intensity VII to VIII shaking occurred in the southeastern corner of the County, and the San Diego coastal zone had intensities of VI to VII.

## FAULTS NORTHEAST OF THE ELSINORE FAULT

**Fault descriptions**. A 12-mile-wide zone on the northeast flank of the Elsinore fault is occupied by three major active fault zones. From southwest to northeast these are the Agua Tibia-Earthquake Valley zone, the Aguanga-San Felipe zone, and the Murrieta Hot Springs fault. These faults are shown on the preceding maps — the Agua Tibia fault along the northeast shore of Lake Henshaw and through San Felipe and Scissors Crossing, and the Aguanga fault north of Warner Springs and through Ranchita.

The Agua Tibia fault crosses Palomar Mountain just west of High Point and along the east flank of Barker Valley to cross the middle of the Lake Henshaw valley. From there it follows S-2 past San Felipe, where it passes into the Earthquake Valley fault. Movement on this zone has put Earthquake and San Felipe valleys under the range of hills on their east flank, along the base of which the faults lie. They cross state route 78 without good exposure just east of Scissors Crossing, and the zone dies out in the Pinyon Mountains 20 miles to the southeast.

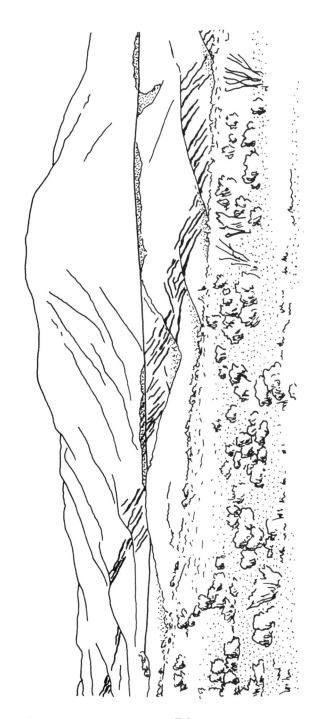

SAN FELIPE FAULT viewed from turnout on highway 78 a mile and a quarter east of Tamarisk Grove junction

The Aguanga fault lies along the northeast flank of the Agua Tibia-Palomar Mountains and is responsible for the steep slopes above Aguanga and Oak Grove. It also passes through Warner Springs, where hot water rises to the surface through fractured rocks along several separate strands of this fault zone. Several miles of S-22 west of Ranchita are lined with road cuts in which the rocks are veined and fractured in the zone of this fault, which crosses the road but is not exposed near the first bend west of town.

Beyond a bend in the Grapevine Hills the Aguanga fault connects with the San Felipe fault. From a large highway 78 turnout on a low crest a mile and a quarter east of the Tamarisk Grove Campground junction (watch for traffic, which travels fast on this road) the crushed and bleached rocks of the San Felipe fault zone can be seen crossing S-3 above the campground. (S-3 is the diagonal line in the illustration.) Five miles east of the junction is another turnout on route 78 at the San Felipe Creek narrows, where you may find printed guides to the Narrows Earth Trail. This trail is entirely within the fault zone, and there are fine exposures of faults at stops 4 and 6 and of crushed and fractured rock throughout the zone. At stops 6 and 7 the main fault puts light-colored granitic rock (to the south) against darker, banded meta-morphic rock. Beyond here this zone breaks into scattered faults, including some of those seen in Split Mountain Gorge.

The Murrieta Hot Springs fault is in the remote mountains northeast of route 79 in the Aguanga-Warm Springs area. It is discontinuous southeastward, where it merges with the San Felipe zone near the San Felipe Creek narrows.

**Future earthquake estimates**. There are no published earthquake risk studies of any of the faults in this zone, but all are thought to be probably active with low slip rates of no more than a few millimeters a year. As individual segment lengths are comparable to those of the Elsinore fault, the faults in this zone presumably are capable of earthquakes in the same magnitude range but with long recurrence intervals.

SAN FELIPE FAULT at stops 6 and 7 on the Narrows Earth
Trail, at turnout on highway 78 five miles east of
Tamarisk Grove junction

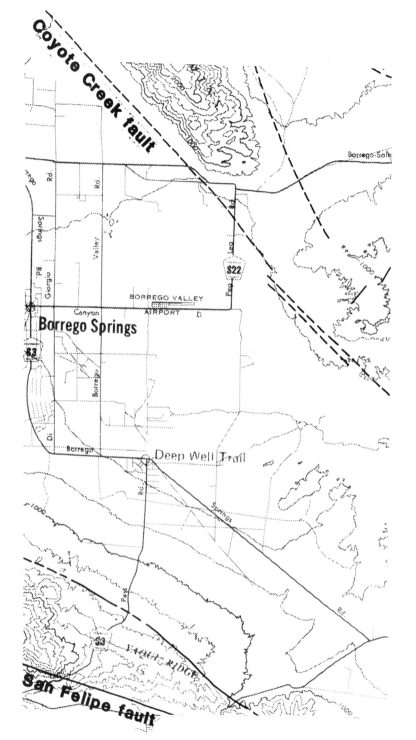

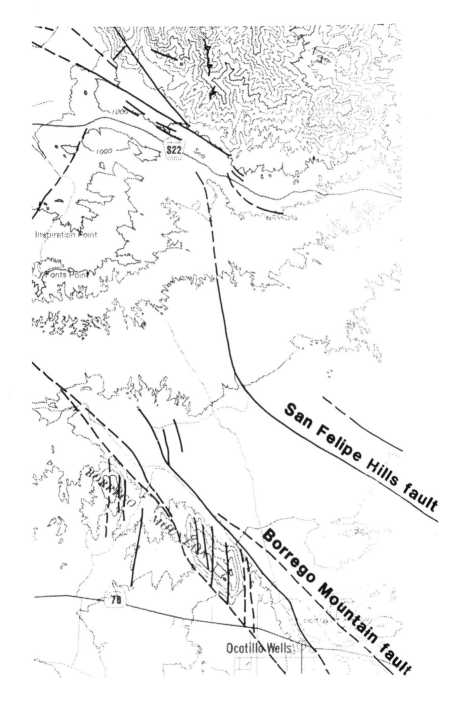

San Felipe Hills fault

Borrego Mountain fault

Inspiration Point

Fonts Point

Ocotillo Wells

S22

78

# SAN JACINTO FAULT ZONE

**Fault descriptions.** The San Jacinto zone is a complex fault system that is some 6 miles wide and 150 miles long, extending from its junction with the San Andreas zone near Wrightwood to the northern edge of the Gulf of California. The zone passes diagonally across the northeastern corner of San Diego County, where it includes the Coyote Creek, Clark, San Felipe Hills, Borrego Mountain, and many smaller, unnamed faults. Part of this zone is shown on the accompanying map excerpts from the 1987 Office of Disaster Preparedness compilation. Among nine segments that have been distinguished along the entire zone, the 20- to 25-mile-long Coyote Creek segment, including the Clark fault, occupies the northern half of the San Diego County part. The Anza gap segment, 20 miles long, adjoins it to the northwest, extending from the bend north of Borrego Springs into Riverside County. Southwest of the Coyote Creek segment the Borrego Mountain segment occupies the next 18 miles, as far as the Imperial County line. The next segment beyond that is occupied by the parallel srands of the 15-mile-long Superstition Mountain fault and the 12-mile-long Superstition Hills fault.

The Coyote Creek fault lies under desert sand coming out of the mouth of Coyote Canyon north of Borrego Springs, but it is exposed in the rocks of the northeast wall in the less accessible upper canyon. To the south the Coyote Creek fault is aligned with the Borrego Mountain fault, which passes through Borrego Mountain and crosses highway 78 at Ocotillo Wells. The epicenter of the 1968 earthquake (magnitude 6.5) was just north of Ocotillo Wells; the fault rupture extended across the highway just east of the road junction, and maximum slip near there was 15 inches.

Among the many branch faults that cross Borrego Mountain, probably the most accessible one is in Hawk Canyon. This is two miles up the Buttes Pass Road, which goes north from highway 78 a mile and a quarter east of the Borrego Springs Road. There are good views of the

BORREGO MOUNTAIN FAULT ZONE. Fault at head of Hawk
Canyon

fault both at the head of the canyon and looking into its
mouth from the Buttes Canyon Road.

East of the Coyote Creek fault the Clark fault passes
southeastward out of Riverside County. It is buried under
the sand across the floor of Clark Valley, but where it is
joined by the Santa Rosa fault along S-22 north of the
Borrego Badlands there are dramatic views of the effects of
recent fault activity. Several prominent cliffs (fault
scarps) in the alluvial fans mark places where recent
earthquakes have displaced these young deposits. Though it
is not visible from the road, the northeast slope of the
raised fault block just a quarter mile from the road at the
Truckhaven Trail turnoff near post mile marker 32 is a
nearly vertical straight scarp 150 feet high and a mile and
a half long.

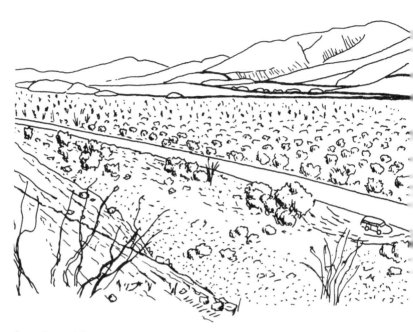

Junction of CLARK and SANTA ROSA FAULTS viewed from toop of bluff on south side of S-22 at turnout west of milepost 34

Two miles to the west at post mile marker 30 there is a geologic exhibit at a turnout on the south side of the road. The view from here up Clark Valley includes two low sandy hills — one near and one far — that were formed by a buckling up of the desert floor by movements along the Clark fault. From this junction of the Clark and Santa Rosa faults the San Felipe Hills fault passes out of the badlands south of the road and on into Imperial County.

**Earthquake history.** The San Jacinto fault is the most active of the southern California plate boundary zones. It has had l3 earthquakes of magnitude near or greater than 6.0 between 1899 and 1987. During that time it has produced more earthquakes in that range than any fault of comparable length in California.

80

# MAJOR SAN JACINTO FAULT ZONE EARTHQUAKES

| DATE | EPICENTER | MAGNITUDE | INTENSITY |
|------|-----------|-----------|-----------|
| 1899 Dec. 25 | Riverside County | 6.6-7.0 | VI-VII |
| 1915 Jun. 23 | Imperial County | 6.3 | V |
| 1918 Apr. 21 | Riverside County | 6.8 | VI-VII |
| 1923 Jul. 23 | Riverside County | 6.2 | V |
| 1937 Mar. 25 | North of Borrego Springs | 5.9 | |
| 1940 May 18 | Imperial County | 6.7 | V |
| 1942 Oct. 21 | Near Borrego Valley | 6.3-6.5 | V-VI |
| 1954 Mar. 19 | Santa Rosa Mountains | 6.2 | |
| 1968 Apr. 9 | Ocotillo Wells | 6.4-6.8 | VII |
| 1969 Apr. 28 | Near Borrego Valley | 5.8 | |
| 1979 Oct. 15 | Imperial County | 6.5-6.6 | |
| 1987 Nov. 23 | Superstition Hills | 6.2 | |
| 1987 Nov. 24 | Superstition Hills | 6.6 | |

From this short historical record it appears that earthquakes of magnitude 6 to 7 are characteristic of the entire San Jacinto zone and that these earthquakes occur at an average interval throughout the zone of 8 to l2 years. The Anza gap segment, just north of San Diego County, has had no earthquakes since the 1890's at least, so it presumably poses a more imminent seismic threat than do the others.

**Future earthquake estimates.** McEuen and Pinckney (1972) estimated a maximum probable earthquake for the San Jacinto fault as a whole of magnitude 6.9 to 7.3, and a maximum credible quake of magnitude 7.6. Assuming earthquake rupture of the entire length of the fault, Woodward-Clyde Consultants (1986) similarly suggested a maximum earthquake magnitude range of 7 to 7.2.

Wesnousky (1986) suggested expected earthquake magnitudes between 6.4 and 6.6 for each of the six segments from the Anza gap in Riverside County southward to the Superstition Hills in Imperial County. Anderson, Agnew, and Rockwell (1989) estimated M6.5 as the maximum plausible earthquake for each of the four adjoining 20- to 30-mile-long segments from north of

Anza to the Superstition Mountain segment in Imperial County, but they also suggested the possibility of multiple-segment quakes up to magnitude 7.2. Rockwell also has proposed that the Anza gap segment may be capable even of a magnitude 7.0 quake, as there has been no large earthquake there at least since 1892. This whole range of estimates is consistent with the 100-year historic record, in which all 13 earthquakes have fallen in a magnitude range of 5.7 to 7.0.

As the Anza gap, Coyote Creek, and Borrego Mountain segments are only 60 miles from San Diego, earthquakes of magnitude 6.0 probably would produce shaking intensities of MM IV to V in the city and VII to VIII in the northeastern corner of the County. Quakes of magnitude 6.5 and 7.0 could shake San Diego at MM V to VI and VI to VII, and northeast County at VIII to IX and IX to X.

## SAN ANDREAS FAULT ZONE

The 150-mile-long southernmost segment of the San Andreas fault extends from Cajon Pass to the Salton Sea. While to the north it is a narrow, well-defined boundary between the North American and Pacific plates, in the Salton Trough the San Andreas splays into a broad zone that includes the San Jacinto, Imperial, and other major faults to the south.

While there has been high seismicity on some of these other faults, the San Andreas in this region has not had a major earthquake in historic times. An excavation at Cajon Pass has provided evidence for at least two, and perhaps four, earthquakes from 1290 to 1805 A.D., and there may have been as many as six quakes there in the past 1000 years. Thus this segment has large earthquakes at least once every two to three centuries, and there appear to have been none here during the past 200 years. As the last quake may have occurred here as long ago as December, 1812, this southern segment is a probable source for the next destructive earthquake in southern California.

Woodward-Clyde Consultants (1986) suggested a maximum magnitude of 7.5 for this segment of the San Andreas fault. Anderson, Agnew, and Rockwell (1989) estimated a maximum plausible magnitude of 7.3 for this segment but up to 8.2 for rupture of multiple segments. A magnitude 8 earthquake on the southern segment could produce intensities of VII to IX in eastern San Diego County and VI to VII in the coastal zone.

# XI. DAMAGING EARTHQUAKES OF MAGNITUDE 6 TO 7 WILL CONTINUE TO STRIKE ALL PARTS OF SAN DIEGO COUNTY

As certainly as the Pacific plate will continue its northward migration past North America, so will crustal rocks west of the San Andreas, San Jacinto, Elsinore, Rose Canyon, Coronado Bank, San Diego Trough, and San Clemente fault zones go on lunging fitfully past rocks to their east. While the huge swarm of northeast-southwest faults on the southern coast has not been active for more than a hundred thousand years, the Rose Canyon fault itself clearly remains active, as apparently do several of its urban neighbors — the La Nacion, those crossing Silver Strand, and perhaps the Florida Canyon and Texas Street faults.

The table summarizes from the text the estimates of maximum magnitude and maximum intensity to be expected from future earthquakes on these faults in or near San Diego County. The message from this table reiterates one that has been repeated many times but always for too small an audience:

In the words of Charles Richter in 1959: "There has been a general impression that earthquake risk does not exist at San Diego, historical records to the contrary being forgotten or ignored...The maximum reasonable intensity during future earthquakes is VIII for the low sandy area on which most of the city, including the business center and the harbor, is situated."

From Michael Reichle, Seismologist with the California Division of Mines and Geology, in 1987: "I would say that there is no place in California that should not be prepared for an earthquake of magnitude 6 to 7."

According to John Anderson, seismologist formerly

at Scripps Institution of Oceanography, in 1987:
"Eventually San Diego will get stronger shaking than any
previously recorded. A quake measuring 6.5 to 7
emanating from the Rose Canyon fault would not be a
scientific surprise."

## MAXIMUM MAGNITUDE AND INTENSITY ESTIMATES
## SAN DIEGO COUNTY

| FAULT | MAGNITUDE | INTENSITY COAST | EAST COUNTY |
|---|---|---|---|
| San Miguel | 6.0 | | |
| Agua Blanca | 6.5-7.2 | VI-VII | |
| | | | |
| San Clemente | 6.6-7.7 | | |
| San Diego Trough | 6.1-7.7 | VI-VII | |
| Coronado Bank | 6.0-7.7 | VI-VIII | |
| | | | |
| Rose Canyon | 6.2-7.0 | VIII-IX | |
| La Nacion | 6.2-6.6 | | |
| | | | |
| Elsinore | 6.9-7.6 | VII-VIII | |
| segment A | 6.8-7.3 | IV-VII | VII-X |
| segment B | 6.6-7.1 | IV-VII | VII-X |
| segment C | 6.8-7.2 | IV-VII | VII-X |
| segment D | 6.5-7.2 | IV-VII | VII-X |
| Laguna Salada | 6.5-7.0 | VII-X | |
| | | | |
| San Jacinto zone | | | |
| Casa Loma-Clark | 7.1 | VI-VII | IX-X |
| Anza gap | 6.4-6.6 | V-VII | VIII-X |
| Coyote Creek | 6.4-6.6 | V-VII | VIII-X |
| Borrego Mountain | 6.4-6.8 | V-VII | VIII-X |
| Superstition Mntn. | 6.4 | IV-VI | VII-IX |
| Superstition Hills | 6.4-6.7 | IV-VI | VII-IX |
| multiple segments | 6.9-7.3 | V-VII | VIII-X |
| | | | |
| San Andreas | 7.3-8.2 | VI-VII | VII-X |

# XII. GOVERNMENT OFFICIALS, COMMUNITY LEADERS, AND INDIVIDUALS CAN MINIMIZE DAMAGE AND INJURY BY PREPARING FOR FUTURE EARTHQUAKES

The lack of strong, damaging earthquakes in San Diego County during this century has been a mixed blessing. We have been spared the death and destruction that have been visited upon San Francisco, Long Beach, San Fernando, and other California cities during that time, but as a result the residents of San Diego County have been misled into a sense of complacency regarding earthquake hazard here. The majority today seem to assume that this part of California has not, does not, and will not have damaging earthquakes, though the older historic record and the geologic evidence show clearly that this is not the case. San Diego County has repeatedly suffered earthquakes of magnitude 6 and higher and shaking intensities as high as MM VII, and similar earthquakes are certain to occur in the future.

Only in the past few years has a concerted effort been made to educate County residents to the earthquake hazard and to encourage preparedness measures. The beginnings of this effort came in 1975, when a county committee, which was convened as a result of the 1971 San Fernando earthquake, issued its report as the Seismic Safety Element of the San Diego County General Plan (San Diego County Environmental Development Agency, 1975). Various earthquake awareness activities were held during statewide Earthquake Awareness Weeks each April through 1986.

In April, 1987, this program was expanded, as San Diego County led the way in developing more extensive informational programs in the state's first Earthquake Awareness Month. That program, and the two annual ones that followed it, were organized by Jan Decker, Director Dan Eberle, and their fellow officials at the San Diego County Office of Disaster Preparedness. Meanwhile former Supervisor Susan Golding had formed the San Diego County Earthquake Preparedness Committee, which, in addition to

86

its task of making recommendations for public policy on earthquake preparedness issues, assumed sponsorship of Earthquake Awareness Month activities beginning in 1988. Every April now there are public lectures and field trips; workshops for hospitals, schools, and businesses; and dissemination of information on earthquake hazard and preparedness measures. Watch for Earthquake Awareness Month events each April.

In the meantime what can you do to prepare for earthquakes to come? Among many sources of information, probably the readiest to hand is the Pacific Bell telephone directory, which has four pages (B9 to B12 in the 1989 through 1993 editions) of its survival guide devoted to earthquake preparedness. Additional information can be obtained from the San Diego County Office of Disaster Preparedness at 5201 Ruffin Road in San Diego (telephone 565-3490).

## XIII. BIBLIOGRAPHY

Anderson, J. G., Rockwell, T. K., and Agnew, D., 1989, Past and possible future earthquakes of significance to the San Diego region. Earthquake Spectra, v. 5, p. 299-334.

Bolt, B. A., 1988, Earthquakes. W. H. Freeman.

Ebersold, D. B. (editor), 1992, Landers earthquake of June 28, 1992: Field trip guidebook. S. Cal. Sect. of Assoc. of Engin. Geol. 1992 Annual Field Trip, 38 p.

Grant, Michael, 1989, Future shake. San Diego Union, March 27, p. E-1, E-5.

Hawk, R. N., and Christiansen, T. P., 1991, City of San Diego ordinances and regulations with respect to geotechnical and geological hazards, p. 137-143, in Abbott, P. L. and Elliott, W. J. (editors.), Environmental perils: San Diego region. San Diego Assoc. Geol., Geol. Soc. America Annual Meeting 1991.

Heaton, T. H., and Jones, L. M., 1989, Seismological research issues in the San Diego region, p. 42-49 in Roquemore, G. (editor), Proc. of Workshop on "The seismic risk in the San Diego region: Special focus on the Rose Canyon fault system". S. Calif. Earthquake Preparedness Project.

Jennings, C. W., 1992, Preliminary fault activity map of California. Calif. Div. Mines and Geology Open-File Report 92-03.

Kern, J. P., 1987 (out of print), Earthquake shaking and fault rupture in San Diego County. Preliminary. report to the San Diego County Office of Disaster Preparedness, 58 pages, fault map of San Diego County.

Leighton and Associates, 1983, Seismic safety study for the city of San Diego, 39 p.

Lindvall, S. C., Rockwell, T. K., and Lindvall, C. E., 1990, The seismic hazard of San Diego revised: New evidence for magnitude 6+ Holocene earthquakes on the Rose Canyon fault zone. Proc. of Fourth U. S. Nat. Conf. on Earthquake Engineering.

McEuen, R. B., and Pinckney, C. J., 1972, Seismic risk in San Diego. San Diego Soc. Nat. Hist. Transactions, v. 17, no. 4, p. 33-62.

Magistrale, H., in review, Seismicity of the Rose Canyon fault zone near San Diego, California. Bull. Seismol. Soc. America.

Mueller, K. J., and Rockwell, T. K., in review, Late Quaternary activity of the Laguna Salada fault in northern Baja California, Mexico. Bull. Geol. Soc. America.

Reichle, M. S., and others, 1990, Planning scenario for a major earthquake, San Diego-Tijuana metropolitan area. Cal. Div. Mines and Geology Spec. Pub. 100, 181 p.

Reichle, M. S., 1991, Earthquake planning scenario for the San Diego-Tijuana area, p. 127-136 in Abbott, P. L. and Elliott, W. J. (editors), Environmental perils: San Diego region. San Diego Assoc. Geol., Geol. Soc. America Annual Meeting 1991.

Rockwell, T. K., and Lindvall, S. C., 1990, Holocene activity of the Rose Canyon fault zone in San Diego, California, based on trench exposures and tectonic geomorphology. Geol. Soc. America Abstracts with Programs, v. 22, no. 3, p. 78.

Rockwell, T. K., Lindvall, S. C., Haraden, C. C., Hirabayashi, S. K., and Baker, E., 1991, Minimum Holocene slip rate for the Rose Canyon fault in San Diego, California, p. 37-46 in Abbott, P. L., and Elliott, W. J. (editors), Environmental perils: San Diego Region. San Diego Assoc. Geologists, Geol. Soc. America Annual Meeting 1991.

San Diego County Environmental Development Agency, 1975, Seismic Safety Element, San Diego County General Plan.

Toppozada, T. R., 1993, The Landers-Big Bear earthquake sequence and its felt effects, California Geology, p. 3-9.

Toppozada, T. R., Real, C. R., and Parke, D. L., 1981, Preparation of isoseismal maps and summaries of reported effects for pre-1900 California earthquakes. Cal. Div. Mines and Geology Open-file Report 81-11.

Toppozada, T. R., Parke, D. L., Jensen, L., and Campbell, G., 1982, Areas damaged by California earthquakes, 1900-1949. Cal. Div. Mines and Geol. Open-file Report 82-17.

Treiman, J. A., 1993, The Rose Canyon fault zone, southern California. Calif. Div. Mines and Geology Open-File Report 93-02, 41 p.

Wesnousky, S. G., 1986, Earthquakes, Quaternary faults, and seismic hazard in California. Journal of Geophysical Research, v. 91, no. B12, p. 12,587-12,631.

Woodward-Clyde Consultants, 1986, Evaluation of liquefaction opportunity and liquefaction potential in the San Diego, California urban area. Final technical report for U. S. Geological Survey Contract No. 14-08-0001-20607.